MACARONI PRODUCTS

Macaroni Products
Manufacture, Processing & Packing

by

Dr. Charles Hummel

1950

LONDON

FOOD TRADE PRESS LTD.

7 Garrick Street, W.C.2

Made and Printed in Great Britain by
GREYCAINES
(Taylor Garnett Evans & Co. Ltd.)
Watford, Herts.

AUTHOR'S PREFACE

For some years past there has been a consistent demand for a technical book covering the manufacture of Macaroni Products and the specialized machinery for this important industry. To fulfil this need the present volume has been written.

Efforts were made to obtain photographs from engineers producing macaroni machinery all over the world, and the Author would like to take this opportunity of acknowledging the co-operation received from those who did send in photographs and descriptive details. The Author hopes to be able to include illustrations of even more machines in any subsequent edition. Special acknowledgment is due to Messrs. Buhler Bros. for their help and co-operation.

The majority of the machines and processes mentioned in this Book are covered by Letters Patent including Patents that are still pending. No mention of Patents has been made as it has been found impossible to make a complete up-to-date list as many items in the Book are protected by patent applications which may lead to Letters Patent at any time.

Lastly, the Author is greatly indebted to Mr. Raymond H. Binsted, Editor of Food Trade Review, for his help and advice in the preparation of the manuscript, also to Mr. A. H. Long, Assistant Editor of that Journal.

CHARLES HUMMEL.

ACKNOWLEDGMENTS

The Author wishes to acknowledge the co-operation of the following firms who have provided illustrations and descriptive details of their plant and equipment for inclusion in this book:

Deit Paslo Emilio Barducci, Milan, Italy.
Blatter, Switzerland.
Braibanti, Milan, Italy.
Buhler Bros., Uzwil, Switzerland and London.
Clermont Machine Corp., Inc., New York.
Consolidated Macaroni Machine Corp., New York.
Mécanique Méridionale, Toulouse, France.
Moriondo & Co., Milan, Italy.
Officine Verrina, Genoa, Italy.
N. & V. Pavan, Venice, Italy.
Premoli & Baudino, Milan, Italy.
Reggiane S.A., Reggio Emelio, Italy.
S.I.G., Neuhausen, Switzerland.
Stige S.P.A., Genoa, Italy.
Tabucchi, Nice, Italy.
Triangle Machinery, U.S.A.
Werner & Pfleiderer, Stuttgart, Germany.
Yberty, Lyons, France.

CONTENTS

INTRODUCTION

THE products of the industry with which we are concerned are only beginning to become popular in England, and consequently the English terminology is not yet firmly established. I propose, therefore, to start by giving the significance of the symbols used. We all know what is meant by Spaghetti, Noodles, and Macaroni, but what shall we call the whole group? The Italians who are the biggest eaters of Macaroni and Spaghetti and therefore should know something about them, call them "Pasta Alimentare" (Alimentary Paste). The Germans call them "Teigwaren" (Paste Goods), and the Americans "Macaroni". I feel that all these names can be misleading and shall use the term "Macaroni Products" as a general name. This name is widely used in the U.S.A., and although it is not entirely satisfactory it is reasonably clear and precise.

Macaroni Products are produced either as plain Macaroni Products or as Egg Macaroni Products. All the different types which I shall now describe may be manufactured as plain or as egg Macaroni Products.

Extruded Solid Macaroni Products

Vermicelli.—Italians call the Vermicelli with the smallest diameter "Cappelli d'angeli" (Angels' Hair). It is the Macaroni Product with the smallest diameter ranging from $\frac{1}{50}$ in. to $\frac{1}{20}$ in.[1]

Vermicelli is generally cut into lengths of about 10 in. and then twisted into curls. It is rarely sold in straight lengths. Recently, short cut scattered Vermicelli has become popular, more especially in France. The average length of the scattered Vermicelli is 1 to 2 in.; this is easy to manufacture and to dry. Satisfactory packing is a problem yet to be solved and is as difficult for short cut Vermicelli as for the twisted variety.

---

[1] *N.B.*—The dimensions—diameter and length—of Macaroni Products vary considerably from one manufacturer to another, and the same shape is often made in quite a number of different sizes. It is, therefore, impossible to give precise figures; all dimensions given are to be understood as mean figures.

Spaghetti.—This most popular Macaroni Product has a diameter of about $\frac{1}{15}$ in. to $\frac{1}{10}$ in. and a length of 10, 20 or 30 in. Most Spaghetti is straight but occasionally it is twisted. It is sometimes short cut to about 1 to 2 in. long and then looks something like very thick short cut Vermicelli. If short cut Vermicelli should become more popular with time, I do not think that this will be the case with short cut Spaghetti.

Noodles.—Extruded Noodles are solid ribbons with a thickness of about $\frac{1}{30}$ in. and in a variety of widths. Narrow Noodles are extruded down to a width of $\frac{1}{20}$ in. Broad Noodles may have widths up to $\frac{1}{2}$ in. and even 1 in. for certain specialities. Extruded Noodles are straight, scattered or twisted like Vermicelli. Straight Noodles are made in lengths similar to Spaghetti, 10, 20 and 30 in. Twisted Noodles are usually about 10 in. long, while scattered Noodles are shorter, having a length of from 4 to 8 in.

Specialities.—Certain specialities may be regarded as belonging to the solid goods, for instance, screw-shaped Noodles, and most of the Macaroni Products made for soups, including letters, numbers, stars, melon seeds, rice, etc.

Extruded Hollow Goods

Macaroni.—Macaroni is the standard product of this type, it looks exactly like Spaghetti with a hole in the centre. The outer diameter of Macaroni may go down to little more than $\frac{1}{10}$ in. About $\frac{1}{5}$ in. is the popular size, but larger diameters up to $\frac{1}{2}$ in. are manufactured in Italy, and in other countries for people with Italian eating habits. The inner diameter should be selected to give a wall thickness of about $\frac{1}{24}$ in. Standard Macaroni is produced in different lengths from, say, 5, 10 and up to 20 in. in special cases. Long Macaroni is always straight and should never be twisted like Vermicelli and Noodles. Macaroni is often short cut with a length of about 2 to 3 in. and the cut can be straight or slanted. Short cut Macaroni usually has a smooth exterior surface but this can be corrugated by utilizing suitable dies.

Elbows.—Elbows look like short curved Macaroni and are sometimes called short cut Macaroni. To make terminology clear and precise, the name of short cut Macaroni should be reserved for the straight short cut Macaroni made on a normal Macaroni die. Elbows are made on a special die with a pin of special design producing the characteristic curve. Elbows

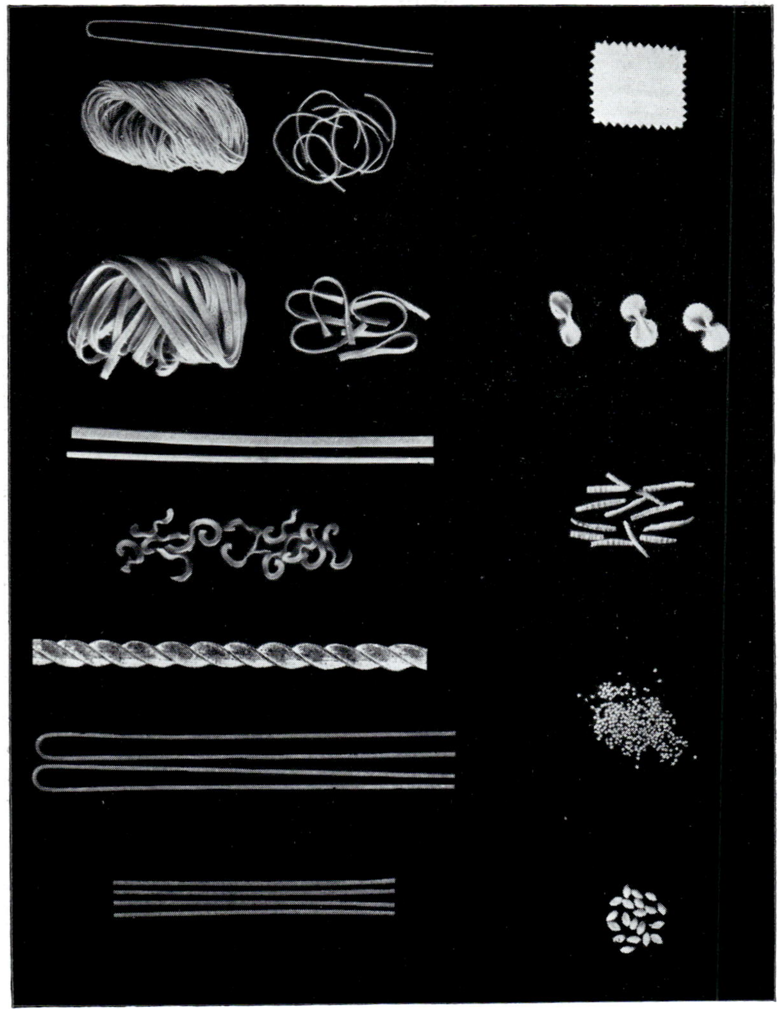

Fig. 1(*a*).—Solid Macaroni Products. From top to bottom— Vermicelli, straight, twisted and scattered; Square Flake; Noodles, twisted, scattered and straight; Bows; Special Noodles; Spaghetti, long and short; Grains; and Melon Seeds.

are cut in lengths of from 1 to 2 in. Elbows are usually produced with the same diameter as straight Macaroni; the more popular outer diameter is between $\frac{1}{6}$ and $\frac{1}{3}$ in. and the thickness of the wall about $\frac{1}{24}$ in. as for the wall of Macaroni. The surface of Elbows is generally smooth but may also be corrugated. On small diameters the smooth surface is more popular, while for large diameters the corrugated surface is more favoured. Very large short cut Macaroni is generally known by its Italian name, "Rigatoni, Canneroni". I shall call them smooth or corrugated tubes according to the structure of their surface.

Specialities for soups are produced when hollow goods are cut very short, as an average less than $\frac{1}{20}$ in. thick. According to the die being used rings, stars, wheels or letters of the alphabet, etc., may be produced.

Certain extruded Macaroni Products do not fit exactly under the heading of solid or hollow goods. This applies more particularly to the many different types of shells with smooth or corrugated surfaces. Most of these products are known in the trade by their Italian name only, as they are not yet widely known outside Italy. Italian speaking people consider that they offer a very different satisfaction to the consumer from most other Macaroni Products. It would, therefore, be advisable for the sake of variety if they were manufactured on a wider scale.

I do not advocate too large a range of different Macaroni Products; there is no point in my opinion for any one factory to manufacture more than eight different sizes of Macaroni. Two sizes should be sufficient to meet any reasonable demand, but eating shells or large corrugated tubes are quite different things from eating Elbows or Spaghetti and justify manufacturing these special products.

Rolled and Cut Macaroni Products

A large proportion of the world's production of Noodles is cut by special cutting rolls, from sheet dough specially prepared for this purpose on machines known as Dough Breakers. The structure of the dough in rolled Noodles is quite different in comparison with extruded Noodles. In rolled Noodles the dough is light and porous, whereas in extruded

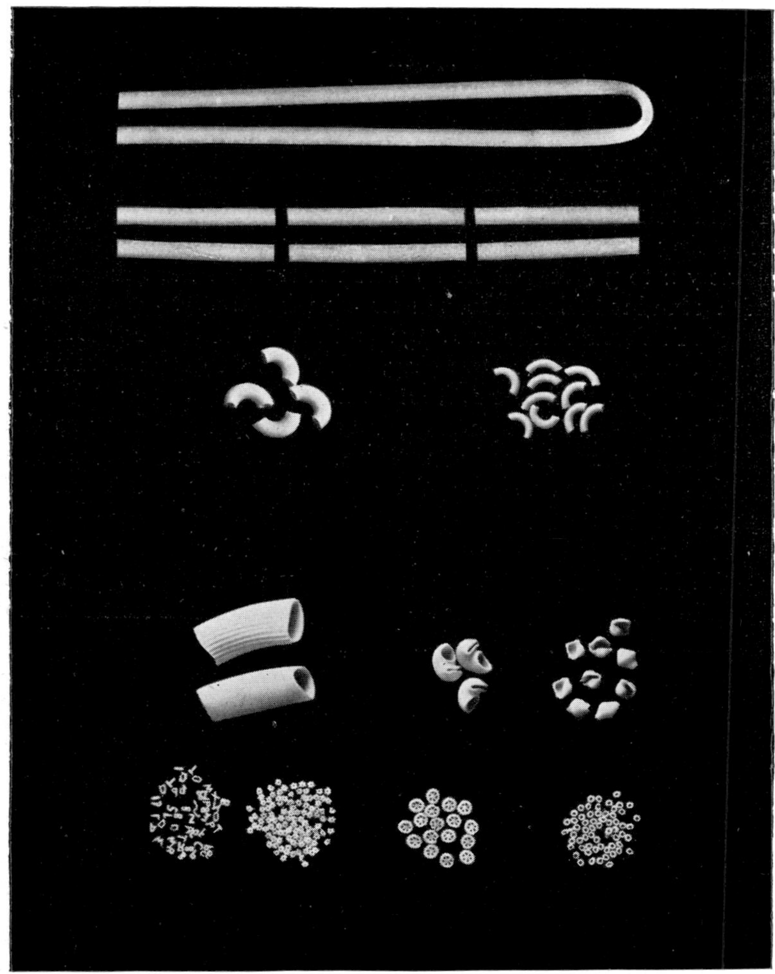

Fig. 1(*b*).—Hollow Macaroni Products. From top to bottom—
Macaroni, long and short; Smooth Elbows, large and small; Tubes,
corrugated and smooth; Shells; Alphabets and Numerals; Stars;
Wheels; and Rings.

Noodles it is more compact and glossy. Apart from the sharp
edges characteristic of rolled Noodles, extruded and rolled
Noodles look the same. Both are made in varying widths and
sold as twisted, straight or scattered Noodles.

Rolled and Stamped Macaroni Products

These are stamped from sheets of rolled dough by special stamping machines. The goods are generally known as "Pasta Bologna", and are produced in different shapes and sizes. Normally they are shaped like bows and I propose to call them by this name. The manufacture of this type of Macaroni Product is usually found to be rather uneconomical. The stamping machines have a relatively small output (approximately 2 to 3 cwt. per hour) when compared with the output of a standard Continuous Extrusion Press (8 to 9 cwt. per hour). A further disadvantage is that up to 30 per cent of dough remains after stamping, which has to be returned to the Breaking Rolls for retreatment.

Ravioli.—Strictly speaking, Ravioli does not belong to the normal Macaroni Products. I mention it only because it is made from the same type of dough as rolled Noodles. Certain manufacturers producing Macaroni Products also make squares of dough which are dried and used for making Ravioli in the home. They look like extremely broad but very short Noodles. As a rule they are square with sides of about 1 in. to $1\frac{1}{2}$ in. and of a thickness of about $\frac{1}{25}$ in.

CHAPTER I

THE IMPORTANCE OF MACARONI PRODUCTS

EVEN without figures to hand no Italian would doubt the importance of Macaroni Products as an item of food; he just could not do without them. Some statistical notes may be of interest to readers and, therefore, are included here.

The consumption of Macaroni Products in different countries varies considerably. According to the latest information available, the approximate figures per year *per capita* are:

Italy	30 to 40 lb.
	(People in Southern Italy eat more than those in Northern Italy.)
France	15 lb.
U.S.A.	8 lb.
England	Figures not available.

Considering the total population of each country this means a yearly production of approximately:

Italy	1,300,000,000 lb.
France	600,000,000 lb.
U.S.A.	1,100,000,000 lb.
England	To be assessed

Exports have not been taken into consideration in the above figures as export business in Macaroni Products for most countries has now lost its importance. Italy and France used to export large quantities of Macaroni Products, Italy once exporting up to 70,000 tons, and France almost 20,000 tons annually. Recently, these figures have dwindled down to insignificance as compared with home consumption in both countries.

The Macaroni Product industry has a tendency to become a home industry in most countries, with the exception perhaps of Canada which is still exporting an important part of her production, more particularly to the British Empire.

The industry is holding its own in Europe; it is spreading and becoming powerful in North and South America, and is developing in England. Macaroni Products are proving a valuable, cheap and handy food; they are acceptable and quickly digested. One pound of a dried Macaroni Product provides approximately 1,600 calories or 6,350 B.T.U.

In recent years the industrial equipment for the manufacture of Macaroni Products has undergone very considerable changes, and has developed from the old-fashioned batch system to a most efficient and practically automatic production line.

Historical Notes

Italy is generally regarded as the original home of Macaroni Products. Certainly it is the country in which Macaroni Products have been and are still most popular, but their manufacture and use seems to have started in China or Japan.

A charming Italian legend, related in a booklet published by "The National Macaroni Institute" of the U.S.A., attributes the discovery of the art of making Macaroni Products to the carelessness of a Chinese maiden. "While busy at her daily task of preparing a batch of bread dough, an Italian sailor courted her so arduously that she forgot her task. Soon the dough spilled from the pan, dripping in strings from the work bench. The strings of dough dried quickly in the sun. The Italian lover, whose name was 'Spaghetti', sympathized with the maiden and thinking to hide the evidence of her carelessness, gathered up the strings of dried dough and took them to his ship. The ship's cook boiled them in broth, and found them most edible. Thus by pure accident was the Macaroni-making process discovered. On his return to his homeland, 'Spaghetti' taught others how to make these tasty and nutritious strings of dough, thus introducing the art of Macaroni-making into Italy, which has since become the greatest consumer of this fine wheat food."

It seems more likely that German travellers learned how to make Egg Noodles during their visits to Asia. They called this food "Nudel", and to this day certain German Macaroni Product manufacturers call their plant "Nudelfabrik". Noodles in Germany are still the most popular Macaroni Product.

In the fifteenth century the Italians learned how to make Noodles from the Germans. The climate of their country, especially the environs of Naples, was particularly favourable for the drying of Macaroni Products, also for the cultivation of the hard wheat from which the Semolina was milled, thus producing rich and tasty Macaroni Products.

The Italian Macaroni Products industry developed rapidly, and quickly spread to France and later all over Europe. Italians settling in America took Macaroni Products with them, and during World War II this industry gained much importance in England.

At the beginning, Macaroni Products were all home-made. A small industry developed first in Italy, and by about 1800 the first mechanical devices for the manufacture of Macaroni Products appeared in Italy. These were very crude and inefficient. Nearly fifty years later the first hand-operated mechanical presses—mainly built from wood—came into existence. More elaborate machines were developed about 1860, most of them driven by animal power, but the increasing popularity of Macaroni Products called for more efficient machinery. This was subsequently developed in Italy and France, and at a later date in Germany.

At the beginning of the twentieth century efficient equipment, comprising Mixers, Kneaders or Gramolas, Hydraulic Extrusion Presses and Drying Cabinets became available. Numerous and efficient plants for the production of Macaroni Products were built, and the home-made goods were replaced by goods produced by an economical process on a commercial scale. Little change was made in the machines in general use for about thirty years, but about 1934 a new development was started. A French firm had already built a simple continuous Extruder, and about the same time in Switzerland and Italy continuously operated automatic Presses were developed, and replaced the batch work of earlier production equipment.

Similar Presses were later built in the U.S.A., and to-day practically all the new Presses installed are of the continuous

B

type. A few years ago continuous operation was proposed for dried Short Goods, and in 1946 a Swiss firm operated the first production line turning Semolina into dried Spaghetti or Macaroni ready for packing in one continuous automatic operation. This production line has yet to be completed by adding automatic weighing and packing equipment. It will then be possible to produce Macaroni Products in a most efficient, economical and hygienic plant, with one man supervising the production of over 6,000 lb. of packeted Spaghetti or Macaroni per shift, all manual work having been entirely eliminated.

CHAPTER II

THE MANUFACTURE OF MACARONI PRODUCTS

MACARONI PRODUCTS are obtained by mixing Semolina with water and kneading this mixture into a homogeneous dough. This dough is then extruded or rolled and cut into the familiar shapes of Macaroni Products—Spaghetti, Macaroni or Noodles.

The Macaroni Products known in Italy as "Pasta Fresca" are not dried, but are sold fresh, ready for cooking, and make the most delicious Macaroni Product dishes. Unfortunately, they have very poor keeping qualities and are awkward to handle. They have acquired a certain popularity in Italy only. In all other countries they are dried and unless otherwise stated, Macaroni Products are always understood to be *dried* Macaroni Products.

Macaroni Products are generally dried to about 13 per cent of moisture content. This means that in 100 parts by weight of Macaroni Products there are 13 parts by weight of water. This water content can be checked by various methods familiar to the food chemist, the standard one being to grind the Macaroni Products to a coarse flour, and then placing this flour in an oven at a fixed temperature for a predetermined time, depending on the equipment and the temperature used; the difference in weight before and after drying, giving the moisture content.

Quicker methods have been developed to give the moisture content in a few minutes, but these are not quite so reliable as the standard method, although sufficient for practical purposes, as we shall see in the chapter on QUALITY AND TESTING.

Once the Macaroni Products have been dried they can be handled with ease and have excellent keeping qualities.

According to the way in which they have been shaped into their final form they are known as extruded, rolled and cut, or rolled and stamped Macaroni Products.

Extruded Macaroni Products are shaped by extruding the finished dough under heavy pressure through a die or mould. According to the size and shape of the holes in the die the extruded Macaroni products are known as Spaghetti, Macaroni, Elbows, Alphabets, etc.

Rolled Macaroni Products are obtained by preparing the dough on a Kneading Machine, like a Gramola for instance, and then the dough is finished and rolled out on a dough breaker to a sheet of adequate size and thickness. This sheet is generally cut on cutting rolls into ribbons of various widths and lengths, thus producing the familiar Noodles.

The sheet of finished dough can also be fed into a Stamping Machine cutting and pressing the dough into the elegant forms known as "Pasta Bologna" or Bows. The sheet of dough may also be run through a Ravioli Machine. This machine deposits little heaps of prepared meat at regular intervals on the dough, covering them with a second sheet of dough, and then cutting the dough between the rows of meat deposits. Cutting is usually carried out along two sets of lines at right-angles to one another; thereby, the two sheets of dough are sealed along the cuts and the result is a ball of meat enclosed in a biscuit of dough, thus producing the product known as "Ravioli".

Plain and Egg Macaroni Products.—Macaroni Products produced by mixing Semolina with water are known as plain Macaroni Products. The dough may be enriched by mixing eggs into it, either fresh eggs or dried or frozen eggs, thus producing Egg Macaroni Products. Some countries require by law that the whole egg be mixed into the dough; in other countries the yolk alone is used.

It is worth recording here that in the U.S.A. Noodles are always supposed to be Egg Noodles. Noodles made from plain dough must expressly be declared as Plain Noodles. The U.S.A. Department of Agriculture has adopted the following definitions and standards for Noodles:

Egg Noodles are the shaped and dried doughs prepared from wheat flour and eggs, with or without water, and with or without salt. The egg ingredient may be whole egg and/or egg yolk. In the finished product the moisture content does not exceed 13 per cent; and the egg content, upon the moisture-free basis, is not less than 5·5 per cent by weight of egg, calculated as whole egg solids. Noodles are commonly ribbon-shaped.

Plain Noodles are the shaped and dried doughs prepared from wheat flour and water, with or without salt. In the finished product the moisture content does not exceed 13 per cent. Plain Noodles are commonly ribbon-shaped.

Seasoned Macaroni Products.—In Italy Macaroni Products are produced with different admixtures to the dough. Fairly popular is "Pasta Verde"—a green Macaroni Product, confined almost exclusively to Noodles, made by mixing Spinach in the dough. Other admixtures have been tried, for instance, cheese, tomatoes, milk, etc., but without having attained any importance. Special Macaroni Products with an addition of gluten are made for diabetics. These are more particularly produced in Italy and known as "Pasta Glutinata".

Coloured Macaroni Products.—Coloured Macaroni Products are accepted in certain countries, while in other countries (U.S.A.) the use of artificial colouring matter is strictly prohibited. With modern equipment there is no need to colour Macaroni Products to make them appear attractive, as such equipment will produce an acceptable Macaroni Product from all Semolina that has been suitably prepared by the Miller. Artificial colouring matter has been used on occasion to shield a defective manufacturing process, and is often used to suggest the inclusion of eggs where only plain Macaroni Products are offered.

Vegetable dyes, like Saffron Annato, have been used, but recently the cheaper coal-tar dyes, Naphtol Yellow S, Orange I and Tartrazine have superseded the vegetable dyes.

CHAPTER III

INGREDIENTS USED IN THE MANUFACTURE OF MACARONI PRODUCTS

Semolina

SEMOLINA is the main raw material used in the manufacture of Macaroni Products. It should be milled from hard wheat only, Amber Durum being the best wheat available for this purpose. Amber Durum was first cultivated in Russia, and Durum seed was imported by Carleton to the U.S.A. in 1900 where the production of this hard wheat increased very rapidly, and in 1928 exceeded 100 million bushels. The same variety is still grown extensively in Russia, in North Africa, the Southern part of Italy, and Roumania. The best qualities are grown under semi-arid conditions, as when cultivated in countries with average or heavy rain, Amber Durum degenerates and produces a grain very similar to ordinary soft wheat.

It is not possible, within the scope of this book, to give a detailed description of the elaborate technique applied in turning wheat into Semolina. Suffice it to note the characteristic qualities which are required.

To produce first-grade Macaroni Products, Semolina should be milled exclusively from Durum wheat. A good Mill equipped for grinding Durum wheat should produce about 65 per cent of first-grade Semolina. It is most important to use Semolina of as regular a granulation as possible with all particles of uniform size. Before the introduction of Continuous Presses, a first-grade Semolina for Macaroni Products was expected to be coarse. However, there is no special point in using coarse Semolina with the modern Continuous Presses. The only advantage of a coarse Semolina is the facility with which its purity can be judged, as undesirable particles of bran and soft wheat are easily detected.

For the manufacture of finest quality Macaroni Products a rather fine Semolina is to be preferred, as it makes the running of modern equipment easier and requires less attention in the blending and mixing process. If fine Semolina is used, this does not mean that it should be of irregular granulation or from a higher milling extraction. A good Semolina should not contain flour.

During the process of mixing Semolina with water, the fine particles will always have a tendency to absorb more than their fair share of water, thereby not leaving enough water for the coarser particles. This will lead to an irregular dough requiring more kneading to produce first-grade Macaroni Products, and excessive kneading, as we shall see later, is not beneficial to the quality. The size of Semolina particles is, therefore, not so important as their regularity. A fine Semolina which is almost flour is not favourable; it will not flow easily and tends to produce dust. There will be trouble in stocking and handling, and the blending device of the Continuous Presses will not run as smoothly and regularly as with a coarser grade.

The importance of using Semolina of regular granulation was recognized years ago by manufacturers of Macaroni Products. This has particularly been the case around the important manufacturing centre of Marseilles, where Semolina is classified and cleaned on Purifiers and the coarse particles reduced to average size on Rollermills. The operation is called "Remoulage", and the necessary plant for this is installed in most of the important factories producing Macaroni Products. This technique has lately attracted the attention of Italian manufacturers, and will certainly help to produce first-class Macaroni Products where irregular or too coarse Semolina must be accepted.

Humidity.—Semolina should have a moisture content of about 12 to 13 per cent (for the definition of moisture see page 19). In most countries the law prescribes a moisture content of not more than 13 per cent, and such Semolina will keep for months without spoiling if stored in a dry, cool place. Higher humidity impairs the keeping qualities and has a tendency to cause Semolina to stick and clog.

Ash.—Ash content should not exceed 0·8 per cent. The percentage of ash gives a fairly reliable indication of the purity of the Semolina, and should therefore receive due attention.

Bran.—Good Semolina should be quite free of all bran particles as these will ultimately appear as brown specks in the finished goods. Particles of bran are particularly undesirable in long Macaroni and long Spaghetti; they are not only conspicuous, but long goods are weakened at the point where bran is included and are much more liable to break during and after the drying process.

Gluten.—The main difference between hard and soft wheat Semolina is the quantity and quality of the gluten inherent in its structure. Semolina produced from good American Amber Durum will contain more than 30 per cent of humid gluten, corresponding to more than 11 per cent of dry gluten. Semolina from a North African wheat will yield as an average just about 20 per cent of humid gluten. The quantity of gluten is not so very important as the quality. Gluten suitable for Macaroni Products should be strong, and may be shorter and less resilient than gluten suitable for bread flour. Gluten is a delicate protein product; it will easily deteriorate under unfavourable conditions and when wet and warm, disintegrates rapidly. Warm, wet gluten loses its strength if kneaded too intensely, and this point must receive special consideration when constructing and running Macaroni manufacturing equipment. I shall revert to this point when discussing the details of manufacturing equipment and the drying process.

A separate chapter is devoted to Laboratory Equipment used in controlling the quality of Semolina.

The scarcity of hard wheat Semolina in most countries during the last ten years has made it necessary to use Semolina milled from the softer types of wheat. As a matter of interest some countries have had to use Semolina from Mills where the flour extraction rate has been up to 90 per cent of the wheat berry. Macaroni Products made from such Semolina have a rather dark colour, and the taste is not so pleasant as that made from hard wheat Semolina milled at a lower extraction rate. The cooking qualities are poor as strength is lacking. This Semolina is generally fine and contains a certain percentage of flour, which necessitates it being handled with special care. The flow tends to be irregular, and it is therefore difficult to blend and make up into a consistently uniform dough. The gluten is of poor strength and efficient drying becomes particularly difficult.

Water

Water used in the manufacture of Macaroni Products should be clear, without taste or odour; it should be reasonably free from micro-organisms and contain only a small proportion of salts. Most water deemed fit to drink will do very well.

The importance of the water has often been exaggerated. A few decades ago when Neapolitan Spaghetti was considered to be absolutely the best, manufacturers trying to make a similar product imported water from Naples, but this did not make better Macaroni Products than those made with local water so long as it was reasonably clean and pure. We must always bear in mind that the water used in the manufacturing process goes into food, and must, therefore, meet the standards for good drinking water. For those who like figures, the following indication may be of value:

After evaporation one litre of water should not leave more than 500 mg. of solids and this should not contain more than:

Carbonate	200 mg.
Sulphate	80 mg.
Silicate	25 mg.
Nitrate	10 mg.
Chlorate	10 mg.
Organic matter	30 mg.

The temperature of the water used in the mixing has a degree of importance. With the batch-type mixers, water of 100° to 160° F. is recommended. The higher temperatures are to be used with the coarser grades of hard wheat Semolina. With Semolina of finer granulation the temperature of the water may be lower. The same applies when using Semolina made from a mixture of hard and soft wheats. Warm water brings out the natural rich yellow of Amber Durum Semolina. The dough will be softer than that made with the same amount of cold water, and softer doughs are extruded with slightly lower pressure and will more readily produce smooth Macaroni Products.

The influence of warm water should not be exaggerated as most of the heat introduced with the water is lost in the older type mixers and kneaders. If due benefit is to be derived from the warm water it will be necessary to heat the cylinder of the Hydraulic Extrusion Presses, and in many cases to heat the dies also. In modern Continuous Presses there is no advantage to be gained by using warm water; the heat generated during mixing and kneading is not dissipated as is the case with the batch-type machines. The dough once formed is immediately extruded, and has no chance of cooling down before passing through the die.

Doughs produced in Continuous Presses easily attain a temperature that develops the best possible colour and texture without using warm water, and, therefore, cold water from the main can be used without disadvantage, except perhaps in winter when lukewarm water will be advisable if the temperature of the water from the main is particularly cold. This may be achieved without extra expense if the cooling water from the cylinder is used for kneading. Needless to say, in such cases the cooling water must comply with the standards mentioned earlier for the water used in making doughs, a condition that is fulfilled in most cases.

Where pure cooling water is scarce and is subsequently to be used in making the dough I would recommend running the cooling water in a closed system, and cooling it in a tank containing a coil through which runs cold water that need not necessarily be fit to drink.

Hot water is not to be recommended for use with Continuous Presses as these machines generate sufficient heat when working. In order that the dough shall not be subjected to unduly high temperatures, the cylinder of the Press must be arranged for efficient water cooling.

Any extra heat introduced with the water will be carried away by the cooling system of the Continuous Press and is a loss in most cases.

Eggs

As far as can be ascertained eggs were first incorporated in Macaroni Products in Germany, and the type of Macaroni Products with which they were used were Noodles. Since then Egg Noodles have become increasingly popular in the U.S.A., to the point that to-day Noodles are always understood to be

Egg Noodles in that country. Noodles without eggs have to be specially labelled as "Plain Noodles". Eggs are now used with all types of Macaroni Products, and Egg Spaghetti, Egg Macaroni, and Egg Elbows are deservedly popular.

Eggs may be added to the dough as fresh eggs (these are naturally considered best), as frozen, or as dried eggs. The quantity of egg which must be added to the dough to make it legal to term the product Egg Macaroni, varies in different countries. In the U.S.A. the Department of Agriculture prescribes not less than 5·5 per cent by weight of egg, calculated on whole egg solids. According to the *Macaroni Journal* the manufacturer should use with every 95 lb. of Semolina, either 5 lb. of dried egg yolk or 20 lb. of whole fresh egg, or $12\frac{1}{2}$ lb. of fresh yolk.

As a rule the egg is incorporated in the dough with the water. Fresh or frozen eggs should be whipped and filtered before they are added to the dough; dried eggs should be mixed with water and the mixture allowed to stand for a few hours before being used.

Other Products

Salt may be added to Egg Macaroni Products in the proportion of 1 to 2 lb. per cwt. Such Macaroni Products keep better and are more tasty. In Italy spinach, cooked and cut very fine, is sometimes incorporated in the dough used for making Noodles. Cheese has also been added, but these goods have not attained much popularity.

Gluten is added to Macaroni Products for Diabetics, thus increasing the total amount of dry gluten up to 25 per cent, as compared with 12 to 15 per cent for the standard product. In certain cases where starch is to be reduced as far as possible, the addition of gluten may be increased to bring the total gluten content up to 30 per cent. Such a dough has exceptional strength, and requires a strong Kneader and heavy pressure in the Extrusion Press. A higher percentage of gluten makes kneading extremely difficult and extruding practically impossible.

CHAPTER IV

BATCH MANUFACTURING PROCESS

Blending Semolina

DUE to the difficulties in obtaining sufficient supplies of first-grade Semolina, it is often necessary to blend different kinds of Semolina to make the best of the available raw materials. If the Semolina has not been blended in the Mill, blending must be done by the Macaroni Product manufacturer.

I strongly recommend the separate storing of each grade of Semolina, and to blend only as required for immediate manufacture. It is always easier to blend them as required, and in this way there is no danger of them getting mixed, a thing which easily occurs when different grades of Semolina are stored in the same bin. Control of stocks is simpler and more accurate and the risk of loss smaller. The different grades of Semolina should be stored in bins, and to obtain a consistent product it is advisable to use a Flour Mixing Machine.

A typical example of a Mixing Machine combines bins and bucket elevators. The feed of each bin into the Mixing Machine can be regulated independently. The different grades of Semolina are thoroughly mixed and discharged into a bucket elevator, and conveyed to the Continuous Extrusion Press, or to the Mixers when the batch process is used. If desired the mixture may be deposited into a bin for further use, an arrangement frequently adopted in Italy.

When using batch Mixers, Gramola and Hydraulic Presses, some manufacturers have considered it advisable to have the bins well insulated and heated so as to obtain a minimum temperature of about 80° F. If the Semolina going to the Mixer is too cold the finished product loses some of the golden colour it should acquire, and it is claimed that the cooking qualities are not quite as good as when the Macaroni Product has been made from warm raw material. This is, however, a debatable point. In any case, the difference can be only small and it would be most difficult to prove as there are so many other factors contributing to the cooking qualities of the finished product. With modern Continuous Extrusion Presses the temperature of the Semolina going to the Mixer does not appear to be of very great importance. On some Continuous Presses the blending of two grades of Semolina is directly and continuously obtained.

All Continuous Extrusion Presses have a measuring device by which a continuous adjustable stream of Semolina is carried into the Mixer. Certain Continuous Presses have two such measuring devices, and each may be adjusted to allow the required amount of either of the two different grades of Semolina to pass to the Mixer. Illustrated is the measuring

Fig. 2.—Measuring device for two grades of Semolina, incorporated on the Buhler Continuous Extrusion Press.

device of the Buhler Continuous Press. Two endless rubber belts convey the Semolina to the Mixer in an even continuous stream. The amount of Semolina can be regulated by setting the speed of the belts, which are driven by a small motor and a continuous variable speed gear-box. A separate lever sets the proportion of Semolina carried on each belt. This system requires a double feed if each belt is to receive a different grade of Semolina. In a small plant, or if the building makes it advisable in a large plant, the Press is kept fed with Semolina by two hoppers. Each hopper contains a different grade of Semolina and feeds a separate measuring system. In factories where Semolina is stocked in bins, or has to be lifted, the Semolina can be carried to each measuring system by an automatic Conveyor.

Dosing and Mixing

In order to produce a good dough, Semolina and water have to be mixed in certain prescribed proportions, for instance, 100 parts by weight of Semolina with a moisture content of 13 per cent mixed with 30 parts by weight of water will give a very good Spaghetti dough. Dough for Macaroni is generally made a little drier, containing, say, 28 to 29 parts of water, while dough for Elbows may have up to 31 parts of water. The exact proportion of water used depends upon the quality of the Semolina, the type of Macaroni Product to be produced and the manufacturing equipment available.

If first-class Macaroni Products are to be manufactured, it is essential that the proportion of Semolina and water should be strictly constant. It is, therefore, necessary to provide adequate means of ensuring correct measurement of water and Semolina. When using batch Mixers the Semolina is weighed on an automatic scale, which is filled from bins. According to the size of the Mixer used, 1 or 2 cwt. are weighed at a time. The scale runs on rails, thus making it possible to feed different Mixers using one scale only. With this system it is also possible to blend different grades of Semolina by filling into the hopper of the scale the required amount of Semolina from different Bins.

As a rule water is measured by volume, using a tank provided with a scale. In order to obtain the required temperature the water is drawn partly from a warm water tank and partly from the cold water main.

Generally, each Mixer is provided with a separate water tank. A thermometer is fitted to the tank as the temperature of the water should be constant. This is important when working with a batch Mixer, if Macaroni Products of regular quality are to be produced. The water tank should be fitted

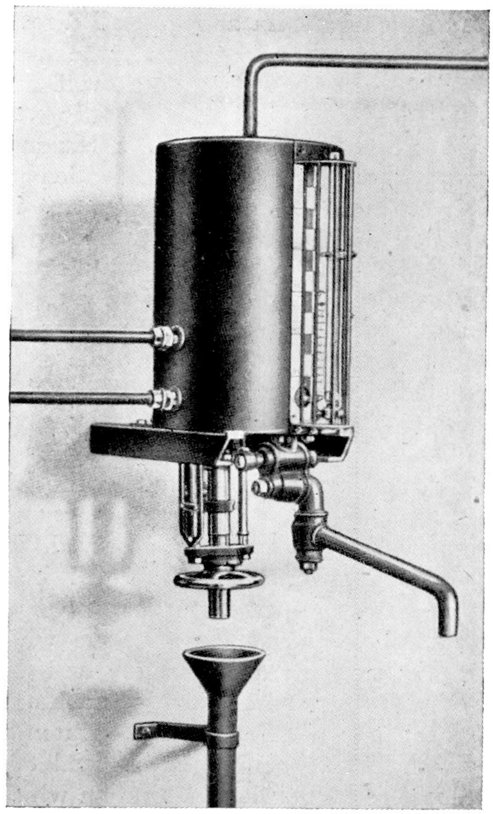

Fig. 3.—Water Tank with scale and thermometer for measuring the quantity of water to be fed into a Batch Mixer.

sufficiently high to enable the water to run directly into the Semolina deposited in the Mixer. It is always advisable to fill the Mixer with Semolina first and to add the water afterwards, as this will do much to prevent the mixture from sticking to the walls and arms of the Mixer.

Much has been said, tried, and printed as to the best method of running the water into the Mixer. The water has been sprayed; it has been run through a pipe with a multitude of small holes, or just poured into the Mixer in bulk. As a matter of fact, it seems to make little difference how the water is incorporated into the mix, but it is important that the water should run into the Semolina and not fall directly on to the body of the Mixer or the mixing arms. If the metal gets really wet the Semolina will stick to it, and will make cleaning difficult.

The most important point is to use a Mixer in which the Semolina and water does not have a tendency to ball up. Such a ball of wet Semolina always has a centre with a moisture content that is well above the average, and an even distribution of the water into the Semolina cannot be attained in the Mixer. If this occurs the even distribution will have to be obtained in the Kneader, and this means extra work for this machine. In many cases the Kneader will not be able to get the water evenly distributed without excessive work, and this tends to weaken the gluten in the dough and may also impair the colour of the finished product. It is necessary for the Semolina and water to remain sufficiently long in the Mixer for the water to be completely absorbed and each grain of Semolina to swell properly. If this point is observed, kneading the mixture into an homogeneous dough will be done easily and quickly, and this is most important.

Mixing is a cheap operation and one which does not interfere with the strength of the gluten and does not spoil the colour. Kneading requires heavy machines which are expensive to run; it tends to weaken the gluten and bleaches the colour, and should therefore be reduced to an absolute minimum. Gluten is a complicated protein which loses what is commonly called its strength when severely kneaded in the presence of water and heat, and this does happen in many Kneading Machines now in use. The strength of the gluten enables the Macaroni Products to keep their shape when cooked, and prevents them from turning into a Semolina paste; it is, therefore, of paramount importance that it is not destroyed in the kneading process.

Mixers have been made by many firms both on the Continent and in the U.S.A., but the design of these machines has not changed for about thirty years. The majority are belt-driven, and have sleeve bearings with bronze bushes, which are grease lubricated. The smaller size, with a capacity of less than 1 cwt. can be tilted by hand. Larger sizes with capacities up to 4 cwt. are tilted mechanically, taking the necessary power from the driving pulley. Tilting is started by engaging a clutch, and generally stops automatically when the Mixer is completely tilted.

In batch Mixers the mixing blades are fitted to a heavy

Fig. 4.—Batch Mixer.

shaft, and have a form as shown in Fig. 4. The shaft runs at 20 to 30 r.p.m.; the cover and the driving-shaft being connected to prevent accidents—the opening of the cover stopping the mixing shaft, except when the machine is in the tilted position. In this position the mixing shaft will run with the cover left half open to allow the Mixer to be emptied. Most Mixers of this type have a sheet-steel body with steel mixing-shaft and mixing-blades, and all parts are carefully machined. The mixing-blades normally keep the walls of the Mixer clear, and scraper blades should be provided at the end of the mixing-shaft to clean the end plates. If this is not done dough will build up on any part of the Mixer which is not being continually cleared by the mixing-blades, and at

C

irregular intervals this dough will fall off and a regular homogeneous mixture will not be obtained.

As a rule high-speed Mixers using small mixing-blades, with a mixing-shaft running at 50 r.p.m. and over, are more

Fig. 5.—Edge Runner.

efficient than the slow-running machines with larger mixing-blades. The latter type are gradually being abandoned as they have a tendency to ball the mixture, which we have seen previously is undesirable.

Edge Runners and Kneaders

From the Mixer the mixture of Semolina and water goes to a Kneader where the dough is produced. The first industrial Kneaders were a type of Edge Runner consisting of a strong rotating pan with a heavy stationary runner rotating on its horizontal axis. To take care of any irregularity in the distribution of the mixture in the pan, the runner is mounted on a crank-shaft so as to rise or sink according to the amount of mixture below it.

The mixture of Semolina and water is tipped into the pan and brought under the runner, where it is crushed into a broad ribbon. Adjustable knives fitted behind the runner cut the ribbon, and an adjustable plough lifts the dough off the pan, at the same time turning it over. As the rotation of the pan brings the dough back under the runner this operation repeats itself. After about ten minutes the mixture of Semolina and water is kneaded into a continuous ribbon of homogeneous dough that covers practically the whole pan. The dough produced in this type of Kneader is as a rule hard and produces Macaroni Products that cook very well, but have a poor and irregular colour. The dough coming from the Kneader is quite cold. The gluten retains all its strength, but the colour is not brought out by heat and is bleached by too long an exposure to the dryness of the atmosphere. The cold, hard dough from the Edge Runner requires a high pressure to extrude it, and therefore strong and heavy Extrusion Presses are necessary. Extruding speed has to be kept low to ensure Macaroni Products with a surface that is not unduly rough, and this means low output from the Extrusion Press.

The Edge Runner type of Kneader is of necessity a very heavy machine and requires strong foundations. The runner when lifted off the pan by a heap of dough falls back heavily when it has passed, setting up vibration in the machine and in the building. All Kneaders of this type have to be erected on the ground floor. However, the majority of this type of Kneader have now been replaced by more modern machines.

At a later date, about 1900, the Edge Runner began to be replaced by a more efficient machine known as the "Gramola", a machine that is to this day the best Kneader available for batch work. Like the Edge Runner the Gramola has a revolving pan, but the runner is replaced by two or three heavy corrugated conical iron workers. These workers are each carried by two spindles, and they can be raised or lowered by worm drives fitted to each spindle. On modern machines the two worm drives belonging to a worker are connected and set by a simple hand wheel. Adjustable ploughs lift and turn the dough after it has passed the workers, ensuring uniform and effective kneading.

The workers are protected by shields and the rotating pan is embodied in a stationary structure, in order to prevent operatives from having their hands and arms caught by the iron workers. Proper attention must be given to these safety devices as the Gramola is well known in the trade as being the most dangerous machine, responsible, together with the Mixer, for almost all the major casualties in the Macaroni Product industry.

The dough produced in the Gramola is of good uniform texture. This machine works fairly rapidly, and, according to the moisture contained in the dough, the time required to produce a perfect batch varies between 5 and 10 minutes. This means that the dough has not so much time to bleach as is the case with the Edge Runner. The heat generated by the kneading is not dissipated as easily, and, therefore, the dough is of much better colour. If properly set the Gramola does not unduly weaken the gluten. Special attention must be given to the setting of the corrugated conical iron workers;

Fig. 6.—Gramola made by Buhler.

they should not be set too low as this would result in too deep a cutting action being exerted on the dough thereby weakening the gluten. For the same reason, too long a kneading time is not to be recommended, and too much kneading will also bleach the dough.

As a rule the mixture coming from the Mixer is tipped directly into the pan of the Gramola. To facilitate this operation the Mixer is generally arranged on a platform above the Gramola (*see* Fig. 75). At the beginning of the operation the workers of the Gramola are set fairly loose and are then lowered by degrees as the dough is being formed. Care should be taken to distribute the mixture regularly in the pan so as to produce a ribbon of paste of uniform thickness. If this is not done the work of the Gramola will be irregular, and high pressures will be developed locally as the thick part of the ribbon passes under the workers, thus setting up vibration which is most detrimental to both the machine and its foundations. Should this occur, however, it is necessary to stop the Gramola, cut the ribbon of paste into small pieces and to distribute them evenly around the pan.

As the mixture is emptied from the Mixer into the pan of the Gramola, the pan must always be kept running. The operator must ensure that the mixture is distributed evenly over the whole pan, and subsequently that it forms into a regular ribbon of dough. Any small pieces of mixture that are not formed into the ribbon of dough, must be brushed on to the path of the workers to be incorporated into the ribbon from the beginning. If this is not done a dough of irregular texture will result, and such a dough will produce striped Macaroni Products of irregular colour and texture.

When the dough is ready the Gramola is usually emptied by hand; the iron workers are lifted and the dough cut into handy pieces with a large knife. The pan of the Gramola should always be stopped for this operation, and the pieces of dough only removed when the pan is not running. Accidents generally occur when cleaning the machine, and, unfortunately, this machine should be thoroughly cleaned after each batch. Dough carried from one batch into the next results in Macaroni Products of irregular texture and quality. In some cases particles of dough left behind may turn sour and get into a fresh batch, thus impairing the quality of the whole batch.

After the dough has been finished on the Gramola, it should be brought into the pot of the Extruding Press as quickly as possible. If this cannot be done, the dough must be covered with a clean wet cheese-cloth to prevent any superficial drying which would result in streaky goods. In certain cases superficial drying may produce hard particles of dough, which are retained in the holes of the die and tear up the goods as they are extruded. This is particularly noticeable when hollow Macaroni Products are produced.

If a fine Sieve made of strong wire is fitted on the die, most of the impurities contained in the dough are retained on the Sieve and the Macaroni Product being extruded will be more regular. This Sieve will save the die from becoming clogged by impurities, and is, therefore, called "Salvatrafile" (die saver) by Italian manufacturers. It is essential to have these Sieves made of wire strong enough to prevent them from being pressed into the holes of the die; the clearance between the individual wires must be fairly small, about $\frac{1}{20}$ in. to retain small impurities. Such Sieves are made specially for the Macaroni Products industry.

Tails and scrapings may be incorporated into the fresh doughs made on the Gramola without appreciable disadvantage, providing that such tailings and scrapings be perfectly fresh and clean. Dough that has commenced fermentation may spoil the whole batch, and the same must be said of dough that has partially dried. Even if such dough can be prevented from clogging the die by using a "Salvatrafile", it is bad practice to use it, as white streaks, due to the partially dried dough, cannot be avoided in the finished product.

The regularity of the dough may be improved by increasing the kneading time, but this as we have seen before is detrimental to the strength of the gluten and, therefore, to the cooking quality of the Macaroni Products.

It has often been proposed that tailings and scrapings should be fed into the Mixer. However, tests have shown that the dough is not changed in the Mixer, therefore, although it does not appear to interfere with the Semolina and water, putting such dough into the Mixer serves no useful purpose. Stale and fresh dough can only be incorporated into a homogeneous dough in the Kneader.

Screw Extrusion Presses

The first Extrusion Presses were built about one hundred years ago in Italy; they were very simple Screw Presses working with one pot and operated by hand. At a later date

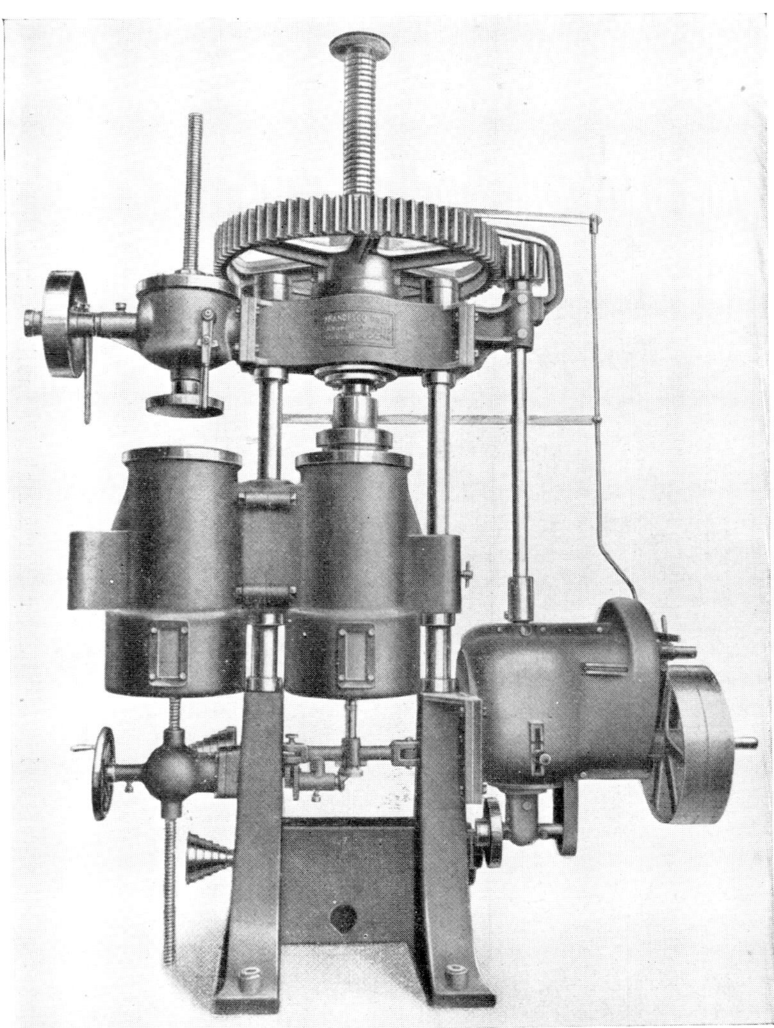

Fig. 7.—Extrusion Press with two pots. Pressure is built up by a screw.

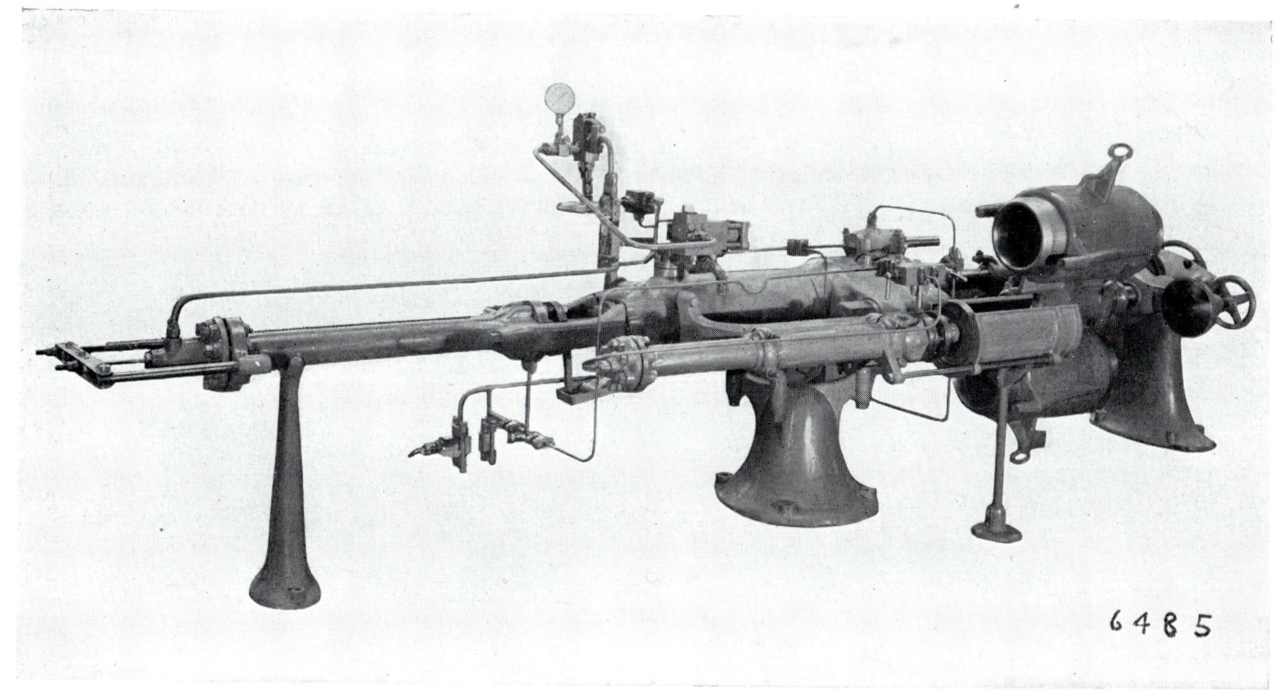

Fig. 8.—Buhler Horizontal Hydraulic Extrusion Press.

Extrusion Presses using two pots were developed in which the pressure is built up by a screw. These Extrusion Presses, from the beginning, were built as Vertical Presses for the production of long goods, and as Horizontal Presses for the production of short cut Macaroni Products.

Screw Type Extrusion Presses are in operation to this day. They operate slowly and are not very efficient, but as the advance of the piston is very regular and independent of the consistency of the dough, they can be used to produce very regular Macaroni Products. In factories still operating them, despite their low efficiency and high maintenance costs, they are mostly used to extrude numerals, alphabets or similar goods, especially when these are produced in only small quantities. These, by the way, are often made from scrapings and trimmings obtained during the manufacturing process of long Macaroni Products.

Hydraulic Extrusion Presses

Some fifty years ago, the Hydraulic Extrusion Press started to replace the Screw type, and up to about ten years ago they were the standard Extrusion Presses in the Macaroni Products industry. Hydraulic Presses are built as Horizontal Presses for the extrusion of short cuts, and as Vertical Presses for the production of long goods.

Some Hydraulic Extrusion Presses have been built with a single pot, but most of the more efficient ones are equipped with two pots. These are mounted on one of the columns of the Press, in order that they can be swung round through 180°. One of the pots is between the columns of the Press and the other outside; the pot between the columns receiving the plunger moved by hydraulic pressure. As the plunger slides into the pot the dough is extruded through the die located at the free end of the pot. The pressure required to extrude the product depends upon the hardness of the dough, its temperature, the extrusion speed, and the die. Warm dough, a soft or moist mixture, needs low extrusion pressures; cool dough, a hard or dry mixture, high pressures. High extrusion speeds go with higher pressure, and in the same way low speeds with lower extrusion pressure.

The pressures required to extrude Macaroni Products

Fig. 9.—Buhler Vertical Hydraulic
Extrusion Press.

through the average die, range as a rule between 1,500 and 3,000 lb. per sq. in. These pressures are very high, and strong substantially built machines are necessary to deal with them. This explains why Hydraulic Extrusion Presses are such large and expensive machines.

While the dough is extruding in one pot, the other pot is charged with large pieces of dough from the Gramola. Most Presses have an auxiliary hydraulic plunger that packs the dough into the pot. This packing has two advantages, it makes it possible to put more dough into the pot and therefore to increase the production of the Press, and to expel most of the air that is left between the pieces of dough.

Air bubbles included in the dough are subjected to the high pressures required to extrude Macaroni Products. Consequently when such an air bubble leaves the die the air suddenly expands and explodes with a loud report, tearing up the goods extruded through the same hole. If the dough has been well packed into the pot, only tiny air bubbles are left which do not break the Macaroni Products during expansion, but leave only a small hole. Such holes are easily found when breaking up dried Macaroni Products, and are particularly easy to see in Spaghetti.

A further trouble, often due to the air included in the dough, is the white streaks which sometimes appear on the extruded goods. They are more obvious on Macaroni and Spaghetti, and are almost always due to air bubbles in the Continuous Extrusion Presses. On Hydraulic Extrusion Presses they are not necessarily due to air bubbles; poor kneading, especially if trimmings have been added to the batch in the Gramola, very often accounts for such defective goods.

In order to completely eliminate air bubbles it has been proposed that Macaroni Products should be extruded under vacuum, a process familiar to the Brick and Tile Industry, in the hope of getting a better and more homogeneous product. Tests, using a Vacuum Press, essentially similar to a de-airing Brick Press, have shown that no advantage is derived from this process that will justify the use of vacuum. This is especially true when using modern Continuous Extrusion Presses and Trim Shredders. These machines, properly adjusted, produce perfectly regular and homogeneous Macaroni Products, even if a fairly large proportion of trimmings have to be used.

When practically all the dough contained in the pot has been extruded, the plunger is pulled back by applying hydraulic pressure to an auxiliary piston situated on the same axis as the main piston. The plunger is stopped as soon as it is clear of the pot; the valves governing this movement being steered by adjustable feelers attached to the plunger itself. This operation is therefore automatic and requires no special attention. When the plunger has cleared the pot, the structure carrying the pot is swung round, and the second pot in which dough has been packed in the meantime moves under the plunger. The valve which admits the hydraulic pressure to the main piston is now operated by hand, whereby the plunger is pushed into the pot and the dough extruded. The structure carrying the pots swivels on ball-bearings, so that one man can easily handle them. Locking screws ensure the correct position of the spot to be put under pressure.

Two systems have been used to locate the die. In the older one the pot has a ring at the lower end, and, the die having a diameter slightly less than the bore of the pot, is introduced from the top and rests on the ring. This system makes it necessary always to use two dies, one for each pot. As it is not possible to run the plunger flush with the die each time a pot has been pressed, the die must be taken out and the cake of dough still adhering to it scraped off, before the die can be reset and the pot filled anew.

To do away with this work the latest type Hydraulic Presses have been fitted with a press table carrying an inset for the die. Two small auxiliary hydraulic pistons press the pot against the table before the plunger starts extruding the dough, thus producing a tight fit between the pot and the press table and preventing the dough from leaking. On this type of Hydraulic Press the steel structure carrying the pots is spring loaded. As the plunger is pulled back the springs lift the pot clear of the press table, making it easy to swing the pot out of position. The die is then easily accessible to scrape off the cake of dough. The second pot which has previously been packed with dough is now brought into position, and extruding can proceed.

With Hydraulic Presses using a press table, special precautions have to be taken when filling the pots, which on this type of machine are open at both ends. For Vertical Hydraulic Presses a charger on wheels is used, and for

Horizontal Hydraulic Presses a stationary charger, into which the dough is pre-packed. The charger is brought to the Press, and its contents forced into the pots by an hydraulic piston, an adjustable cover closing the pots at the other end. This cover is hand-operated on small presses, and set by hydraulic pressure on the larger ones.

Hydraulic High Pressure Pumps

Hydraulic Extrusion Presses are operated by water under

Fig. 10.—Vertical High Pressure Pump with two plungers.

high pressure; the pressure used depending upon the ratio
between the area of the piston and the area of the plunger,
and on the pressure to be applied to the dough. If piston and
plunger have the same diameter, the water pressure is the
same as the pressure on the dough, and may vary between

Fig. 11.—Horizontal High Pressure Pump with three plungers
and water tank.

1,500 and 3,000 lb. per sq. in. If the diameter of the piston is
smaller than the diameter of the plunger, the water pressure
will be higher, whereas if the diameter of the piston is larger,
which would be exceptional, the water pressure will be lower.

The necessary water pressure is produced by special high-
pressure pumps. These are built in two types, Vertical Pumps
and Horizontal Pumps. The smaller ones, mostly Vertical
Pumps, have one cylinder, while the larger types have up to
four cylinders. They are equipped with a safety device which

lifts the admission valve when the pressure exceeds a predetermined load.

Accumulators

The pumps may deliver the high-pressure water direct to the Extrusion Press or to an Accumulator. Pumps that deliver direct to the Press are often fitted with cylinders of different diameters. So long as the plunger of the Extrusion Press has not packed the dough too tightly into the pot, the large cylinder will deliver a strong flow of water under medium pressure. As the plunger finds a stronger resistance on the dough, the small cylinder takes over the delivery of water under the now required high pressure. Thus it is possible to speed up the work of the Extrusion Press without using too powerful a pump. When the pump delivers the high-pressure water directly to the Press, one pump is necessary for each Press.

In larger plants it is more economical to feed the Presses from an Hydraulic Accumulator, the Accumulator being

Fig. 12.—Pneumatic Accumulator with three steel containers.

charged by the pump. By this means a large amount of high-pressure water is always available, making it possible to keep the whole plant in continuous operation. The demand on the pumps is regular, a large pump doing the work of several small ones with less power and less maintenance costs. The older type of Hydraulic Accumulators are loaded with actual weights in cast iron or heavy concrete. These require heavy foundations and occupy a large amount of valuable space. The amount of high-pressure water that can be accumulated is somewhat limited, and it is not possible to increase the capacity at a later date if required.

The modern Pneumatic Accumulators have a number of interchangeable steel containers. One container is filled partly with water and partly with air at high pressure, the remainder being filled with air at the same pressure. When pressure water is used from the Pneumatic Accumulator, the air expands and maintains the pressure on the water at almost the same level. By regulating the proportion of water and air in the container, the variation of the water pressure can be held within prescribed limits. The high-pressure pump delivers directly into the container of the Accumulator which has been partly filled with water. Safety devices are provided, which cut off the pump when the Accumulator is filled. This safety device may be used with both types of Accumulators.

Pneumatic Accumulators must be provided with a small Compressor to produce the high-pressure air when starting, and to replace the air that has been lost whilst operating.

Cutting Short Cut Macaroni Products

Short goods are cut as they are extruded by a rotating knife. By using a variable speed drive the speed of the knife can be set to suit the length of the goods to be produced. Some of the first variable speed drives used were constructed from two belt-driven conical pulleys. More recently, variable speed motors and other mechanical and hydraulic variable speed drives have been used (P.V. drive, Arter Variator).

To get a wider range of the length of cut, knife-holders with two or more knives may be fitted, the cutter for short cut goods being essentially the same for Hydraulic Presses and for the modern Continuous Extrusion Presses. I shall revert

to this point in more detail when discussing the modern
Continuous Extrusion Presses.

Handling Fresh Short Cut Macaroni Products

As they leave the die, short cut Macaroni Products are
received on a Preliminary Drier from which they proceed

Fig. 13.—Cutting Spaghetti by hand as it leaves the Continuous
Extrusion Presses.

to the final drying, or are handled immediately by a Pneumatic
Conveyor or Bucket Elevator. For further details see chapter
on methods of DRYING MACARONI PRODUCTS.

Spreading Long Macaroni Products on Sticks by Hand

For the production of long Macaroni Products the older
types of Screw and Hydraulic Presses were always Vertical
Presses. With the modern mechanical Extrusion Presses, the
cylinder may be horizontal or vertical, but the die must be
horizontal in all cases.

The long Macaroni Products are allowed to extrude about
4 ft. in length, a bunch is then taken in the left hand of the

D

operator and cut with a large knife held in the right hand. The long goods are then put on suitable sticks, and distributed evenly by hand. This work requires a certain amount of practice, but after a short time the operatives, often girls, acquire a remarkable dexterity.

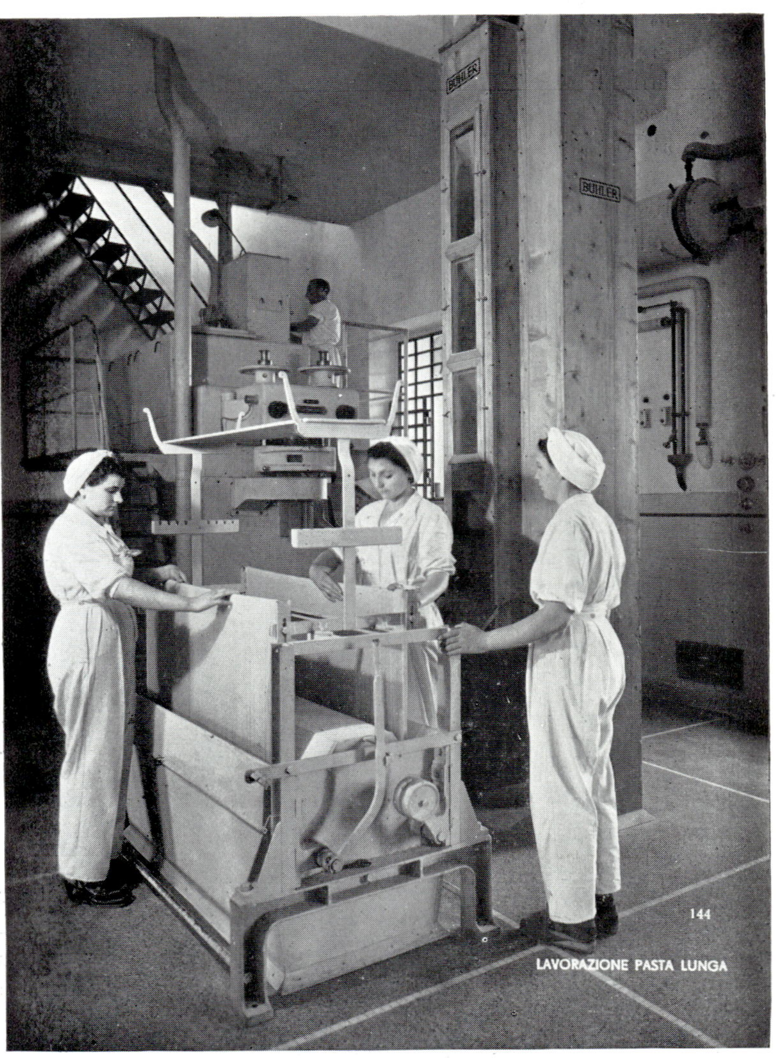

Fig. 14.—Trimmer for Long Macaroni Products.

The long Macaroni Products on the sticks are necessarily of irregular length. On all types of Presses the extrusion speed is not absolutely regular over the whole surface of the die, thus producing Macaroni Products of uneven length. Furthermore, it is practically impossible for the operator always to cut the Macaroni Products at exactly the same length, and to distribute them on the sticks so that both sides are of the same length all over the stick.

Macaroni Products of regular length are most desirable as they fill the Drier more completely, thereby assuring better output from the Drier, and subsequently giving a better package. The sticks should, therefore, be placed over a Trimmer, and the goods cut to equal lengths. On most Trimmers the knife is operated by hand, but some have built-in motors. All Trimmers are built on similar lines, the important difference being in the construction of the knife. The older types have a long knife operated by an eccentric, and clip off the trimmings over the whole length of the stick at the same time. A more recent construction has a rail, on which is affixed a travelling knife which cuts the Macaroni Products. A third system, used mainly in America, trims Macaroni Products with a Cutter similar to a Corn Reaper.

Long Macaroni Products on sticks should be of even length before they are loaded into a Drier.

Twisted Macaroni Products

Twisted Macaroni Products have been popular for many years, and have retained a remarkable degree of popularity to the present day. Actually, there is little to say in their favour apart from the neatness of their appearance and being an established practice.

Twisted Macaroni Products are twisted by hand, or mechanically by a Twisting or a Folding Machine. Twisting by hand involves a considerable amount of manual labour. An experienced girl may twist about $\frac{1}{2}$ cwt. per hour, according to the regularity of the flow of the Macaroni Products from the Extrusion Press and the skill of the operator. The amount of trimmings resulting will vary up to 5 per cent.

Macaroni Products of this type are easily handled, which from the manufacturer's angle, is a point in their favour.

Normally they are dried on trays, but do not dry quite so readily as scattered Macaroni Products. Where the strings of dough overlap drying is slower, and care must be taken to avoid fermentation of the dough at these points. The dried twisted Macaroni Products must be handled and packed by hand.

For the production of larger quantities of twisted Macaroni, both Twisting and Folding Machines have been developed. The Twisting Machine receives the strings of dough extruded by the Press, and twists them into a shape very similar to the curls made by manual labour. The Folding Machine receives the ribbons of dough from a Noodle Cutter, and folds them into shape slightly different from the hand-made article.

Fig. 15.—Double Twisting Machine made by Mécanique Méridionale, Toulouse.

Twisting Machines are of two different types, one is fed by hand with a regular supply of strings of dough already cut to their appropriate length, and these are twisted and deposited by the machine in regular rows on a tray. This Twisting Machine is of simple contruction, and fairly easy to operate.

It may be used with any type of Extrusion Press, and will handle all kinds of twisted Macaroni Products. As a rule three girls are required to operate the Twisting Machine, one girl cuts and prepares the strings of dough coming from the Extrusion Press, a second girl feeds the strings to the Twisting Machine, and the third handles the trays. The output of this machine is about 2 cwt. per hour.

Another type of Twisting Machine is combined with the Extrusion Press, and receives the strings of dough direct from the specially arranged dies. One of the most successful machines of this type is the Twisting Machine of the Mécanique Méridionale, Toulouse. This machine has two arms, each having a set of dies and twisting equipment incorporated. The dough is cut into suitable lengths, and is fed by hand to a Belt Conveyor which carries it to the extrusion worm of the Press. The dough is pressed by the worm into the two arms, each of which carries a set of small round dies, each die having a number of holes in proportion to the size of the strings of dough required. As the strings leave the die they form a bundle that is cut and twisted into its final shape by the machine. Incidentally, let us note here that this is the first time the Continuous Extrusion Press for Macaroni Products has been mentioned.

The Twisting Machines produce curls very similar to the hand-made product, and can be set for the production of large or small curls. The output of such a twin unit is about 5 cwt. per hour; the machine requiring one girl to feed the strip of dough, and two girls to handle the trays. They require a Mixer and Kneader for the production of the ribbon of paste to be fed into the worm of the Press. The trimmings, that cannot be completely avoided, go back to the Kneader or are used to produce soup paste on a small Extrusion Press. Recently, such Twisting Machines have been combined with Continuous Extrusion Presses.

The combination of four Twisting units with a large Buhler Press equipped with Trim Shredder, and pneumatic return of the trimmings to the Mixer of the Press, has proved to be a very efficient and successful unit. With this unit labour is reduced to supervision of the Continuous Extrusion Press and the handling of the trays. The Trim Shredder of the Buhler Press combined with pneumatic transport takes care of the trimmings, so that practically every pound of Semolina delivered to the Press goes into the finished product. The output of such a unit is 6–8 cwt. per hour according to the size of the curls to be produced.

One of the most difficult problems on the Twisting Machine is to ensure the even flow of the strings of dough from all the individual dies that make up a set. If the flow from one die is too slow, the bundle coming from this die will produce incomplete curls; again, if the extrusion speed is too fast, the percentage of trimmings will increase. To ensure a steady even flow, the arms carrying the dies are jacketed and heated by steam or hot water. Hot water is preferable owing to easier control. The latest type machines are fitted with electric heating with automatic temperature control. It is necessary to subdivide the heating device into different sections, and to have an independent temperature control of each section. The proper distribution of temperature is most important for an even flow of dough. Pressure on the dough inside the arm is fairly uniform as the hydrostatic loss due to speed and friction is small compared with the total pressure; a condition which is due to the large section of the arm as compared with the circumference and to the low speed, about 3 ft. per minute, inside the arm.

The extrusion speed mainly depends on three factors, the pressure on the dough, the dimension of the die and the channel carrying the dough to the die, and the viscosity of the dough itself. The pressure, as we have just seen, is fairly uniform. The die and the channel carrying the dough to the die, cannot be changed easily to regulate the flow, therefore, the most convenient way of regulating the extrusion speed is to alter the viscosity of the dough by changing the temperature. Dough is a bad conductor of heat, and it is possible to heat the dough locally, thereby only changing the viscosity and extrusion speed in the immediate vicinity of the heated part. This gives us the possibility of regulating the extrusion speed fairly easily.

During kneading and extruding, different temperatures are produced in the dough. For instance, the outer part of the dough coming from the Gramola cools more quickly than the inner part and with Continuous Extrusion Presses, the dough in contact with the extrusion worm gets warmer than the dough running against a cold cylinder wall. During the short time available the temperature in the dough mass cannot become uniform, as would be the case with a good heat conductor, or with a fluid of low viscosity in which heat distributes fairly regularly by convection.

In order to further control the extrusion speed, the Mécanique Méridionale use a mechanical device to obtain a more even flow of the dough strings from the various dies. Rings are inserted in the arm just before each die, the inner diameter of the ring being chosen to give a regular extrusion speed. The rings and dies are then numbered to allow for identification, which makes it easier to fit them into their proper place when they have been removed for cleaning.

To fold noodles, a Folding Machine is used, which receives the noodles as they are delivered by the Noodle Cutter. It is, therefore, usual to combine Calibrating Rolls, Noodle Cutter and Folding Machine into a self-contained unit. The output of such a unit is about 4 cwt. per hour, which is nearly double the production obtained on the French type of Twisting Machine. As the noodles are cut from a solid sheet of dough they are automatically of uniform length. The noodle Folding Machine therefore produces practically no trimmings. These machines do not twist the noodles into the regular curls made by hand, but folds the noodles into strips in length the same as the width of the sheet of dough. The folded noodles are handled like twisted noodles during drying operations. The strips are broken into convenient lengths for packing, which produces some broken products that offsets part of the advantage gained of producing no trimmings prior to the folding operation.

Rolled and Cut Macaroni Products

The most popular Macaroni Product to be rolled and cut is Noodles. Blending, mixing and kneading of the dough from which noodles are produced is substantially the same as for extruded goods. The raw products are Semolina and Flour milled from hard wheat and Amber Durum. Hard Wheat Flour is the standard raw material for noodles in the U.S.A., and is a very popular raw material in most other countries. Amber Durum Semolina is used more particularly

Fig. 16.—Dough Breaker, with one pair of rolls and a clutch for
running the rolls forwards or backwards.

in Italy, especially when producing extruded noodles. In the
U.S.A. noodles must be made with eggs (see the definition of
noodles by the U.S.A. Department of Agriculture, page 20).

The noodle dough produced on standard Mixing and
Kneading Machines receives less kneading than a similar dough
for extruded Macaroni Products, and is finished on a Dough
Breaker. The Dough Breaker consists of a pair of rolls mounted
on a suitable frame. The bearings which carry the rolls are
adjustable, and can be set by a hand-wheel so as to vary
the gap between the rolls. An indicator fitted to the adjusting
device of the rolls gives the width of the gap. The dough
coming from the Kneader is pressed into the nip of the rolls,
and pulled into the gap between the rolls by friction. The
piece of dough is then forced through the gap, and rolled
into a sheet having a thickness corresponding to the setting
of the rolls. This operation is repeated several times, setting
the rolls closer together as the dough is rolled, the dough
thereby becoming more uniform and plastic.

Different systems are used to make the handling of the sheet of dough more convenient. Using one pair of rolls a table is provided on each side, and by using straight and crossed belts to drive the rolls in connection with a clutch or a double belt shifter, the rolls may rotate clockwise or anti-clockwise. This

Fig. 17.—Clermont Reversible Dough Breaker.

enables the operator to pass the dough in succession backwards and forwards through the rolls as many times as he considers necessary without changing position.

The manufacturers of the Clermont Reversible Dough Breaker describe the working of that machine as follows:

"Only one operator is required on the Clermont, because its tables are short and have rollers at the end which turn freely. While the dough sheet is thick there is

Fig. 18.—Buhler Dough Breaker with two pairs of rolls and two common tables.

sufficient room for it to pile up on the tables. However, when the dough is worked out into a long thin sheet, it passes over the rollers and falls on a small bench set at either end between the table and the floor. Here it piles up neatly, folding automatically in zigzag form. When the rollers are reversed, the sheet piles up similarly on the opposite bench. As the dough sheet feeds through, it unfolds automatically in rising from the bench to the table, running true and smoothly to the rollers."

The illustration opposite shows a Dough Breaker equipped with two pairs of rolls. These rolls are connected by two common tables, and always run in one direction. The dough from the first table runs through the first pair of rolls, it then passes on the second table to the second pair of rolls, and is delivered by these rolls back to the first table, where the working cycle starts again. As the rolls in this type of machine always run in one direction, no time is lost in reversing the rolls and consequently a high output is obtained.

The non-reversible Dough Breaker normally requires two operators, one on each side of the machine. However, a non-reversible Dough Breaker that is run by a single operator has been developed by the Clermont Machine Corp., who give the following description of this machine and how it operates:

"This machine is similar in design to our Reversible Dough Breaker with the exception of the tables, the belt conveyor and other necessary changes. With the reversible machine, each time the dough passes from one table to the other, the direction of the rollers must be reversed. With the non-reversible machine, the rollers run continuously in one direction.

"The non-reversible Dough Breaker is equipped with a short straight table at the operator's end, while on the opposite end is a tilting table with a trap-door bottom which is opened and closed from the operator's side by a lever. Underneath is an inclined canvas belt conveyor. At the end of this conveyor is a large table provided with a centre support to ensure its rigidity. It is also equipped with a dough-winding attachment.

"*Operation.*—The rollers are opened to their maximum, and the trap-door is also opened. Two or three pieces of dough from the Kneader about 18 in. long are fed through the rollers, one piece at a time. These will fall on the belt conveyor, which will automatically bring this dough back to the operator. The operator then lowers the rollers about 1 in., feeds the dough pieces through again, one piece at a time, and again they will be returned to him automatically, this time in a thick sheet form. Now two or three pieces are placed on top of one another and fed through the rollers again. Then the rollers are lowered another $\frac{1}{2}$ in. and the dough sheet fed through again. This sheet is doubled and fed through the rollers. This operation is repeated several times until the sheet is smooth and silky. At this stage the trap-door is closed and the rollers are lowered to an opening of $\frac{3}{16}$ in. for the thickness required by the Calibrator of the Noodle Cutter. The

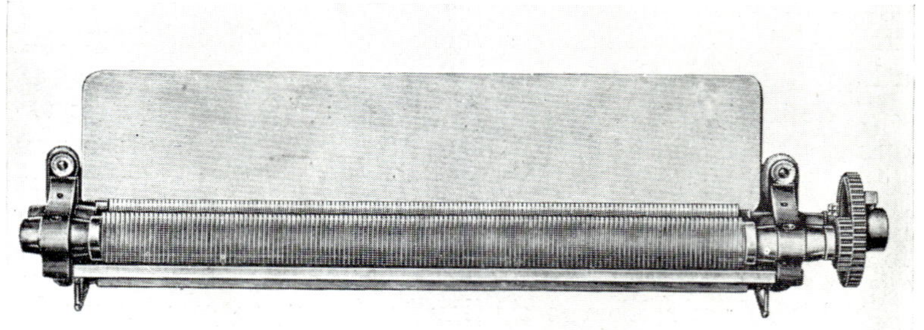

Fig. 19.—Cutting Rolls for Noodle Cutter made by Braibanti.

dough spool furnished with the machine is placed on the dough winding attachment which winds the dough automatically, this is then carried to the Noodle Cutter."

On all Dough Breakers the gap between the rolls may be set, according to the work to be performed, by a hand-wheel which acts on the bearing housings at both ends of the rolls. This setting device keeps the rolls parallel, and only their distance apart is changed.

The finished dough coming from the Dough Breaker is finally rolled into a roll, and fed into the Calibrating Rolls. These Calibrating Rolls are usually incorporated into a common frame with the Cutting Rolls. On the Calibrating

Rolls the sheet of dough is rolled out to the exact thickness required, and the calibrated sheet is then cut into ribbons by the Cutting Rolls. The ribbons are lifted out of the grooves of

Fig. 20.—Noodle Cutter with two pairs of Calibrating Rolls.

the Cutting Rolls by a special comb, cut into strips of uniform length by a rotating knife, and dropped on trays in readiness for drying.

A pair of Cutting Rolls may be seen in Fig. 19. The grooves on the Rolls are made in different sizes so as to produce noodles of varying widths. The Rolls are fitted into a small frame and may be changed easily, making it possible to use the same equipment for the production of noodles of different widths.

A quick changing device has been developed by Clermont, who describe it as follows:

"A complete set of standard rollers carefully adjusted and ready to use is carried on a single drum, which can hold three, four, or five sets of rollers. To change the rollers the operator simply pulls out the button located on the front of the drum, turns the desired rollers into position and then snaps the button back into position."

The noodles coming from the Noodle Cutter are dropped on to trays, where they are distributed regularly by hand or by a mechanical Spreader. The important thing is to shake the noodles up and spread them evenly, they will then curl up into all sorts of different shapes forming a kind of screen which allows the air to circulate freely between the ribbons, thus ensuring quick and uniform drying.

Mechanical Noodle Spreaders are often combined with a feeding device for the trays, which are taken from a pile and fed under the Spreader as required.

Fig. 21.—Fancy Stamping Machine

To produce folded noodles the Spreader is replaced by a folding machine, which automatically deposits the noodles in regular strips on the trays.

The quality of rolled noodles, apart from the raw material used, depends to a considerable extent on the careful manufacture of the sheet of dough. The dough coming from the Kneader after having been kneaded only the shortest possible time, should be rolled as quickly as possible. Long exposure

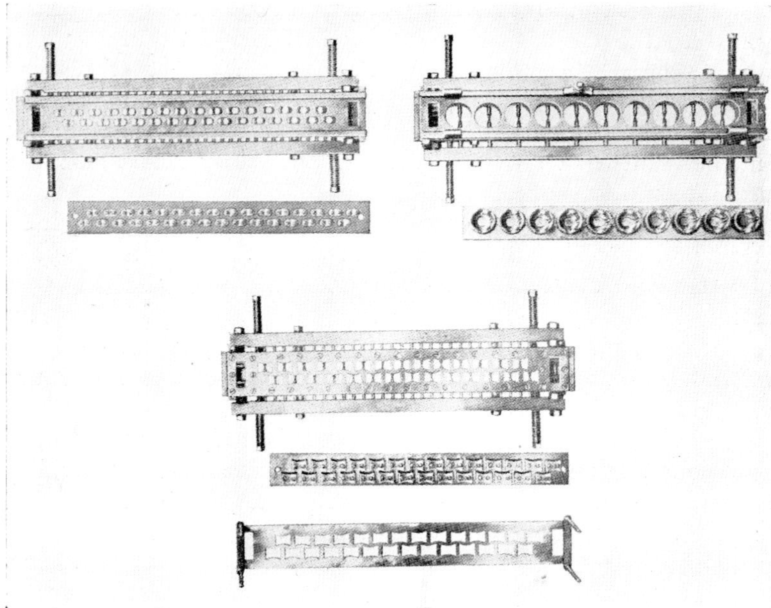

Fig. 22.—Dies for Clermont Fancy Stamping Machine.

to the air will bleach the natural golden colour of the dough. Superficial drying will have the same effect, and produce noodles having undesirable streaks of different shades. The rolls should not be too cold as this will make it almost impossible to get the desired silky finish. It has, therefore, been proposed that the rolls should be heated before starting, which may be done by using a small electric radiator. Once the rolls have the appropriate working temperature the friction set up by rolling the dough is generally sufficient to maintain this temperature.

Rolled and Stamped Macaroni Products

Rolled and stamped Macaroni Products are produced in much the same way as rolled noodles, the only difference being that the roll of dough from the Calibrating Rolls goes into a Stamping Machine instead of going to a set of Cutting Rolls. Fig. 21 shows one of the Stamping Machines, which are specially made in the U.S.A. and Italy. The sheet of dough runs into a set of feed rolls where the dough is calibrated to the final thickness, and fed at the appropriate speed to the oscillating Stamping die. Large Stamping dies run at slow speeds but require a large amount of dough, whilst smaller dies, although they usually run at higher speeds, require less dough. It is, therefore, necessary to have an independent drive on both the Calibrating Rolls and the oscillating Stamping dies.

The finished product coming from the Stamping Machine is shaped in the form of bows of different sizes and styles, according to the type of die being used. Normally, different styles of bows are produced on the one Stamping Machine by merely changing the die. Particular care has, therefore, been taken by the manufacturers of these machines to make the changing of the dies quick and foolproof.

A die consists essentially of a "male", "female" and "stripper". The male or punch, is made of high quality phosphor-bronze mounted on a steel plate. The female, or die, is made throughout of high-grade steel. Each individual punch fits accurately into the die, resulting in a clean-cut bow. The stripper, of sheet brass, is fastened to the die.

Each die is provided with four screws for fine adjustment. Locking washers and nuts hold these screws fast, thus preventing the pins from getting out of set. The die opening adjustments are similarly protected.

From the die, the stamped bows fall on to a Conveyor, which carries them to the trays on which they are spread and dried like scattered noodles.

In comparison with Extrusion Presses, the output of machines producing stamped Macaroni Products is rather low, only occasionally exceeding 3 cwt. per hour. A considerable percentage of the dough has to be returned to the

Dough Breaker, but the actual figures depend upon the size and style of the bows being produced.

Like all rolled goods, the colour of the bows does not come up to the rich attractive colour of goods produced on a Continuous Extrusion Press. Manufacturing costs are higher than for most other types of extruded Macaroni Products, yet in certain regions, due to their original style, they find a market that cannot be neglected.

Ravioli

Ravioli as a finished article does not come within the scope of the regular manufacturer of Macaroni Products. We have seen that in certain cases square flakes of dough are being prepared for the production of Ravioli. These flakes may be produced as very broad short noodles.

As a rule they are made on a special Square Flake Machine. This machine consists of a pair of Calibrating Rolls to ensure even feed and uniform thickness of the dough, a small Noodle Cutter with grooves of appropriate size, and a rotary knife which cross cuts the noodles after they have been slit by the Cutter. The Flake Machine is usually arranged to take a 10-in. dough sheet. When the sheet is produced on a normal 20-in. Dough Breaker, a knife is inserted in the centre of the table between the flattening rollers and the dough-winding attachment. The two 10-in. sheets are then wound as if they formed a single sheet. An offset bracket on the Square Flake Machine making it possible to feed one half of this sheet at a time, the spool being reversed to feed the second 10-in. sheet.

From the Flaking Machine, the square flakes are received on trays exactly like scattered noodles and dried in the same way.

E

CHAPTER V

CONTINUOUS MANUFACTURING PROCESS

Development of Continuous Process

IN the previous chapter I have described the machines used in the manufacture of Macaroni Products according to the classic batch process. This technique originated in Italy, and subsequently spread throughout the world.

Until about 1935 practically all Macaroni Products were made according to this batch process. The mechanical equipment had attained a very high degree of efficiency, and there seemed little scope for further progress except in the perfection of minor details, when rather suddenly a new continuous manufacturing process was evolved, and which, developing with surprising rapidity in less than fifteen years, completely changed the manufacturing technique of the Macaroni Products industry. Prior to 1935 continuous manufacturing processes had been suggested in various quarters, but without reaching industrial application, except in one single case.

The first industrial Continuous Extrusion Press was the Tabucchi Press. This Press invented and manufactured by Tabucchi was installed in the Albertini Works at Nice in France in 1919, and continues to operate to the present day. In the Tabucchi Press pressure is built up by rolls.

The further development of this type of Extrusion Press proved to be rather difficult, and a few years later was abandoned. All the efforts of the manufacturers of equipment for the Macaroni Products trade turning to the Continuous Extrusion Press building up pressure with a worm. These new machines proved to be the prototype of quite a new range of manufacturing equipment that within ten years completely revolutionized the manufacture of Macaroni Products, and made Mixer, Kneader and Hydraulic Press obsolete and out of date.

Operations that had previously been performed by individual machines were handled by a single unit comprising a

Fig. 23.—First Continuous Extrusion Press built by Tabucchi.
Pressure is built up by two rolls and the extruded Macaroni
received on cardboard on an oscillating table.

continuous feeding system for Semolina and water, a continuous
Mixer and a continuous Kneading and Extruding device.

Three fundamentally different types of Continuous Extrusion Presses have been designed, each having its own system
of building up the required pressure on the dough. The
systems used are the following: Rolls—Worms—Worm
combined with piston action.

The first industrial Continuous Extrusion Press, the

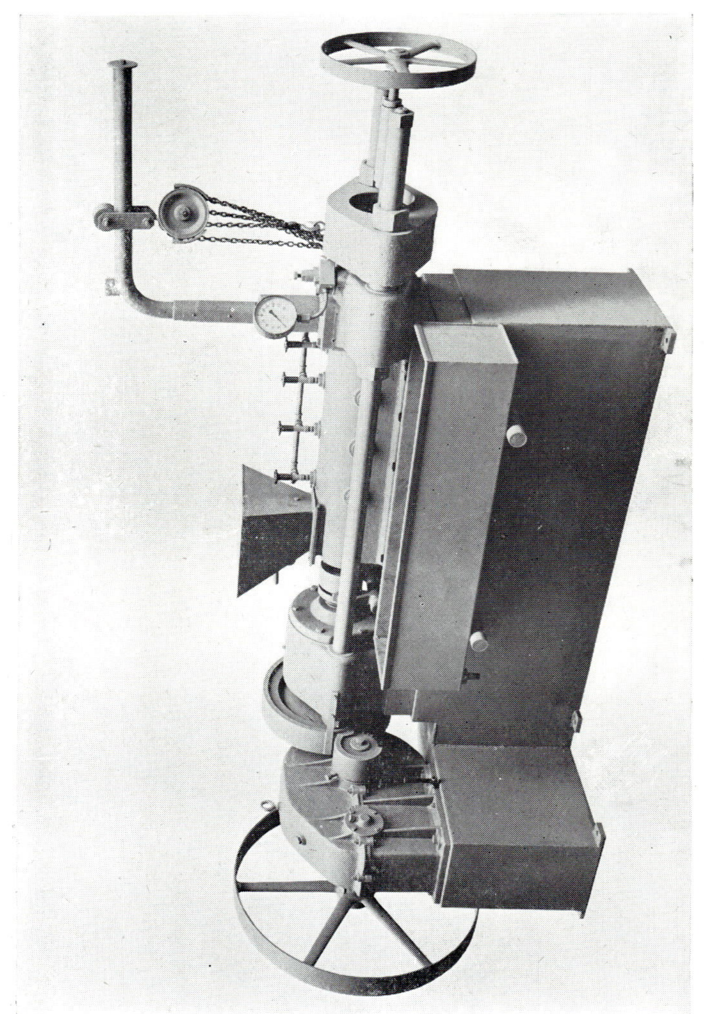

Fig. 24.—First Buhler Continuous Extrusion Press kneading the dough and building up pressure with a Worm.

Tabucchi Press, built up the necessary pressure with a pair of rolls.

In 1934, Buhler supplied their first Continuous Extrusion Press kneading the dough and building up the necessary pressure with a worm. At about the same time Braibanti put on the market their Automatic Press, in which pressure was built up by a worm having an oscillating longitudinal movement superimposed to its normal rotation. Of these three types one has gained outstanding importance. With one exception, all the manufacturers of automatic Extrusion Presses use the worm principle.

The rolls used by Tabucchi found no further application for many years, but have lately been incorporated in the large Clermont Automatic Press. The combination of worm and piston action has been completely abandoned. In their new machines Braibanti use normal rotating worms.

CONTINUOUS EXTRUSION PRESSES

Building up Pressure with Rolls

The principle of building up pressure with rolls has been used in Extrusion Presses in other industries for a very long time. Years ago Pug Mills or Extruders were used in the manufacture of bricks and tiles, in which the pressure necessary to extrude the clay through the die was built up by a pair of corrugated cylinders.

The first, and for many years the only application of this principle to the manufacture of Macaroni Products was due to Tabucchi. Water and Semolina are properly mixed in a batch Mixer, and the mixture delivered to two rolls situated on the same horizontal plane. The mixture of Semolina and water adhering to the rolls is forced through the gap and into a chamber, limited by part of the surface of the rolls and an elongated die. Due to the high pressure between the rolls and in the dough chamber, the mixture is worked into a regular dough and extruded through the die as Macaroni, this being the only type of product produced by Tabucchi on their Continuous Press. The Macaroni produced on this Press is of remarkable quality, but difficulties have been experienced in building larger machines of this type.

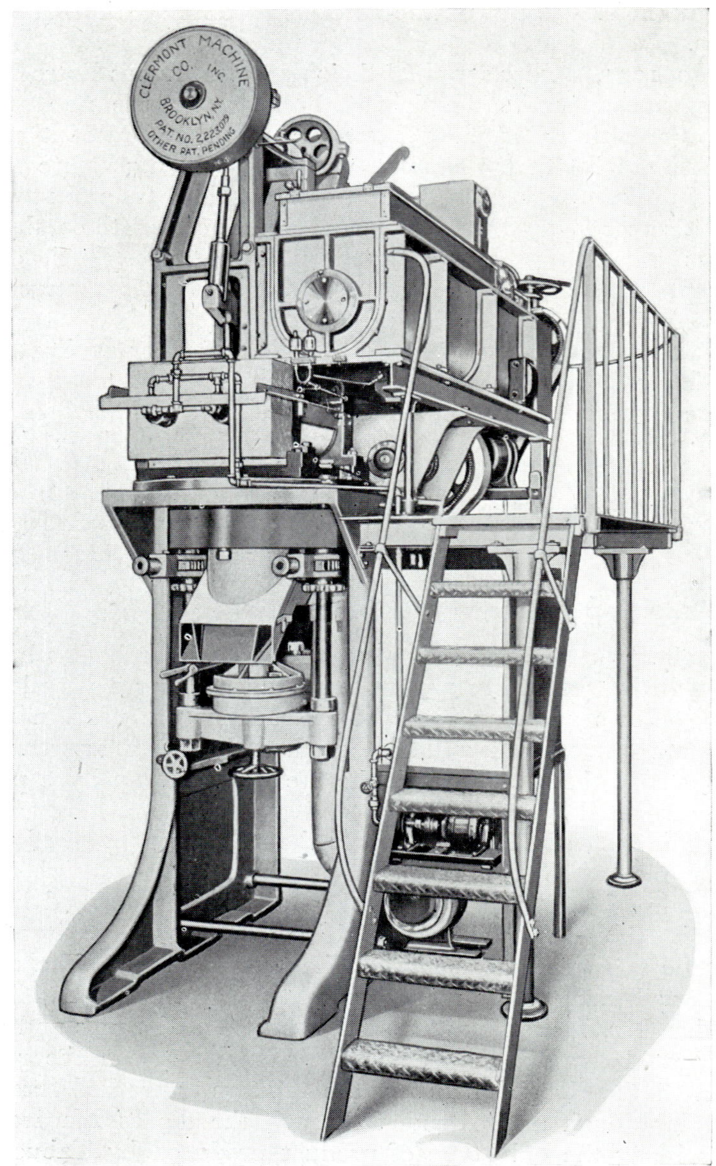

Fig. 25.—Clermont Automatic Continuous Extrusion Press
building up pressure with rolls.

The total pressure on the rolls is very high, and difficulty was found in designing adequate bearings to withstand the heavy pressure developed in the dough chamber. A very strong frame is necessary as pressure is exerted over a large area. This design is not capable of dealing with such heavy pressure as the cylinder of the Continuous Extrusion Press using a worm, or the pot of the Hydraulic Press.

Furthermore, difficulty was experienced with the die. Keeping the die tight proved difficult, and changing the die required considerable effort. For these reasons the construction of this type of Press was abandoned for a time, but some years ago was renewed by the Clermont Machine Corporation.

This machine, according to the details given by the manufacturers, is built for the production of both long and short goods and is equipped with a Continuous Dough Mixer. Flour or Semolina is introduced by a special feeder adjustable from 0 to 1,200 lb. per hour, and the water is fed, by means of a very sensitive valve, in the correct proportion. A hot and cold water mixing valve is provided, and the makers recommend that the water going to the Mixer should have an average temperature of 105° F. The Dough Mixer thoroughly mixes the ingredients, and then automatically feeds the dough to a pair of rolls which work out the dough into a thin sheet, exactly as it is done on a standard Dough Breaker. This sheet of dough is then delivered to a second pair of rolls, a small chamber being provided at the bottom of these rolls. At the bottom of the chamber there is a die holder carrying the die.

The dough sheet accumulates in the small chamber and when it is full a pressure develops which forces the dough through the die. A pressure gauge is attached to the chamber thus enabling the same pressure to be maintained the whole time, which ensures that the quality is maintained and no variation in texture of the Macaroni occurs. The feeding of the dough sheet to the chamber is continuous.

The Press takes a die $15\frac{1}{2}$ in. in diameter, with a $14\frac{1}{2}$ in. working surface. Dies of other sizes may be used by placing a special ring on the die holder. The ring is easily removed when not required. The Press is equipped for high and low speeds, and is easily adjusted from one speed to another.

The low speed produces 1,000 lb., and the high speed about 1,200 lb. per hour.

Building up Pressure by a Worm Combined with Piston Action

The first Continuous Extrusion Press made by Braibanti built up pressure by a unique combination of worm and piston action.

Water was measured by a water pump, and the amount of water delivered regulated by using a variable amount of the total stroke of the piston. Semolina was measured by using a bottomless container connected by a flexible pipe to the hopper receiving the Semolina. The container has an oscillating movement, and an opening which can be regulated by a slide movement. With every oscillation a quantity of Semolina is delivered, depending upon the position of the slide. Water piston and container are driven from a common crankshaft, so that water and Semolina are always delivered together. Both ingredients are mixed in a continuous Mixer, and the mixture is delivered to a pair of rolls acting in a manner similar to that of the Dough Breaker.

From the rolls the dough, which is beginning to be formed, goes to a horizontal worm where kneading takes place. At the end of the worm the dough enters the vertical extruding cylinder. This cylinder contains two worms, which rotate and at the same time have an alternating vertical movement. The die is located at the lower end of the cylinder. During the upward stroke the rotation of the vertical worms screw them out of the dough, and at the same time the dough arriving from the horizontal worm is pushed into the vertical cylinder. During the downward stroke the worms, acting like pistons, force the dough through the die.

This Press gave a good production, but proved too complicated to build on a large scale and to maintain in good working order. It was difficult to stop the dough from leaking at the rolls, and the drive of the oscillating worm proved rather troublesome.

In later models the rolls and the oscillating movement of the vertical worm were abandoned, and the Continuous Extrusion Press built by Braibanti to-day uses a normal worm

Fig. 26.—Modern Continuous Extrusion Press made by Braibanti
incorporating built-in Pre-Drier.

to build up the pressure necessary to extrude the dough through
the die. The characteristic shape of the Braibanti machine,
due to the vertical compression worm, has been maintained
in all the larger models built by this well-known Italian firm.

Building up Pressure by Worm Action

With the exception of the Clermont machine, all the Continuous Extrusion Presses now on the market, and there are more than twenty different types, use a rotating worm to extrude the dough. A very large proportion, in certain countries almost 90 per cent, of the extruded Macaroni Products are now produced on such Presses, and I shall now consider in greater detail the construction and working of such Presses.

Feeding and Blending Semolina

The Continuous Extrusion Press requires a regular and steady feed of Semolina. Most machines have a single feeding system, and, therefore, if Semolina is to be blended this should be done on a Flour Mixing Machine combined with bins, as explained in connection with the batch system (*see page* 28) where this problem has been discussed in detail.

An exception is made in the construction of the Buhler Press, which is supplied with a twin feeding system for Semolina and Flour. This makes it possible to blend two grades of Semolina and/or Flour as they are fed into the Press. Whether a single or double feeding system is used the regularity of the feed is of paramount importance. First-class Macaroni Products must be perfectly regular in colour and texture, and this regularity can be achieved only by using a well-blended dough, which will be obtained only if the proportion of water and Semolina are always the same. This explains why it has been necessary to use so much ingenuity to perfect the feeding device.

Almost every large manufacturer of equipment for the Macaroni Products industry has developed a feeding device of his own. Strange to say, the principle of all the different systems is the same. Semolina or Flour are measured by volume, and practically all the known continuous mechanical means to achieve this result are being used.

I have already mentioned Conveyor Belts as used by Buhler. On the smaller types the feed is regulated by changing the speed of the belts, which are driven by a variable speed drive. Whereas with the larger types the speed of the Conveyor Belts is constant, and the section of the stream of Semolina is regulated.

Other firms use a Conveyor worm, and regulate the speed at which the worm is rotated. The "Reggiane" (Reggio

Emilia, Italy) use a remarkable device, which is a combination of the feed for Semolina and water whereby the proportion of Semolina and water is adjusted independent of the output required, and the output regulated by changing the speed of a single shaft without interfering with the proportion of water and Semolina. On the shaft of the worm measuring the Semolina a water wheel has been fixed, which picks up a certain quantity of water at each revolution and delivers it into the Semolina. The quantity of Semolina carried by the worm is proportional to its angular speed, as is the amount of water delivered by the wheel. Changing the angular speed, therefore, changes proportionally the quantity of water and Semolina simultaneously. The proportion of water and Semolina are regulated by changing the depth at which the wheel dips into the water.

On certain other Continuous Extrusion Presses Semolina is measured by a rotating table, and the quantity of Semolina regulated by adjusting the scraper or changing the speed of the rotating table.

Recently, especially in Italy, very simple feeding devices for Semolina have been used, consisting essentially of a wheel which extrudes the required amount of Semolina through an adjustable orifice. This construction is very simple, and has the further advantage of using a larger inlet for the Semolina, a feature of importance to all manufacturers using fine-grade Semolina or Flour, as these have a tendency to clog when conveyed through small tubes or ducts.

Vibrators.—Another group of feeding devices incorporates Vibrators, the most remarkable being the Vibrator developed by Soder, in which the flow is regulated by changing the amount of the vibration. The flow delivered by the Vibrator is of remarkable uniformity, and can be regulated with astonishing precision. The vibration is generated by electro magnets, and the current to feed them by an electronic valve. The frequencies used are fairly high for a mechanical device, being about 50 to 60 oscillations per second.

On some Continuous Extrusion Presses the feeding system for Semolina is interlocked with the feeding system for water. We have seen how in the Reggiane machine the speed of a single shaft is regulated to control the flow of both Semolina and water, but no provision is made to give an alarm when the

Fig. 27.—Double Soder Vibrator for feeding two separate products into the Mixer of a Continuous Extrusion Press.

supply of water or Semolina fails. Other manufacturers supply, on request, their Continuous Extrusion Presses equipped with a control unit which gives an alarm signal if the supply of water or Semolina fails and cuts out automatically the ingredient that is still arriving. This makes it impossible to flood the Mixer, or accidentally to have a mixture so dry that the pressure built up to extrude it will endanger the Press.

Even with these latest precautions the feeding systems for measuring Semolina or Flour by volume are not perfect. The most regular dough is obtained by blending water and Semolina by weight. The specific weight of Semolina varies according to the size of the individual particles, and how it has been packed. A really satisfactory feed, therefore, can be obtained only by using some sort of automatic scale making blending by weight possible. This scale will further provide a very simple means of controlling the quantity of Semolina passing through the Continuous Extrusion Press.

Feeding Water into the Mixer

Practically all the Continuous Extrusion Presses use one of the following principles to feed the required quantity of water into the Mixer. They measure by volume, or use the flow of water through a given orifice. Water is measured by volume using a pump with variable stroke or driven at variable speed, or a water wheel as with the Reggiane Press. In the latter case the quantity of water is regulated either by changing the depth of the water in the tank in which the water wheel is immersed, by varying the speed of the wheel, or the positioning and number of buckets. With the principle involving the flow of water through a jet, the quantity is regulated by changing the height of the water column above the measuring jet. As the flow depends upon the square root of the height, in other words multiplying the height by four only doubles the flow, this system gives the possibility of regulating the water flow very accurately.

Due care should be taken to use a jet with a hole of the correct diameter. For this reason the Buhler Press, which uses this principle, is delivered with two jets of different diameters. The construction can also be reversed by using water under constant pressure flowing through an orifice of variable section. Constant pressure is usually obtained by using a water tank in which the water level is maintained at a fixed height, either by overflow or by a ballcock acting on the valve through which the water is admitted to the tank. From the tank the water is measured by a needle valve, the position of the needle or pointer regulating the flow. These different systems may all be set to work satisfactorily. Measuring with a jet or needle valve requires no drive, and therefore no moving parts, but the water is delivered under very low pressure and the water tank must be installed above the Mixer of the Press. A drive, and therefore more moving parts, are required when the water is measured by a pump or a water wheel. With a pump, the water tank may be installed in the most convenient place, even below the Mixer if required, which makes it possible to reduce the height of the Extrusion Press.

With the Continuous Extrusion Press the remarks concerning the best way of incorporating the water into the Semolina (*see* page 31) also apply. The water can be sprayed by means of pipes containing rows of fine holes, but this calls for water under fairly high pressure and holes that do not become clogged too rapidly. The water can also be delivered through a larger diameter pipe, an arrangement that will work with any dosing device.

Experience has shown that it is immaterial how the water goes into the Mixer, but it is the correct proportion of water and Semolina that is of paramount importance; therefore, the open pipe being the most simple device is becoming more generally used. There is, however, one point which must be taken care of, as we have already found when discussing the batch Mixer; the jet of water must be delivered into the Semolina and not against the metallic parts, shaft, mixing arms, or trough of the Mixer.

The Continuous Mixer

The first Continuous Mixers used were modified Batch Mixers, with a longer mixing trough of smaller diameter. Water and Semolina were fed in at one end, and the mix delivered at the other. With time and experience two different types of Continuous Mixers were evolved; one type retained the principle of a single mixing shaft, and sub-divided the Mixer into two or more units. A typical example, as used on an Italian Continuous Extrusion Press, has a small Pre-Mixer into which water and Semolina are fed. From this small Mixer the mix is delivered into a normal sized Mixer, and passes a second similar Mixer before going into the kneading worm.

A construction using two parallel shafts with interweaving mixing arms was introduced by Buhler. The mix from this Mixer may be delivered either directly into the kneading worm, or into a small one-shaft Mixer acting as a feed to the Continuous Extrusion Press. The single shaft construction has the advantage of being mechanically simple, the drawback being the tendency, already noted (page 32), of these Mixers to ball up the mix of Semolina and water. This is particularly disagreeable on Continuous Extrusion Presses, as a mix which has become balled up has not only a somewhat irregular water distribution, but it is almost impossible to feed it regularly into the kneading worm. By utilizing two or more Mixers, the mixing time can be increased so as to give each particle of Semolina adequate time to completely absorb its share of water.

The double-shaft construction is more complicated mechanically, but has the important advantage of not balling up the mix. A perfect distribution of the water is thus obtained, and the mix retains an almost granular structure and feeds very evenly into the kneading worm. On Presses using a one-shaft feed Mixer, care must be taken not to allow this feed Mixer to receive too large a quantity of mix, as in this case balling up will certainly result. The quantity of mix inside the Continuous Mixers must be adjusted to the type of Mixer used, the Semolina, and the proportion of water and Semolina. In the Mixer each particle of Semolina must get its share of water, and be allowed the necessary time to absorb the water and to swell completely. On the other hand the mix is not to be kneaded into a dough or allowed to ball up. A double-shaft Mixer can be filled almost to overflowing and work perfectly, giving the Semolina all the necessary time to absorb the water. The one-shaft Mixer should not be more than half full, or just sufficient to cover the shaft. This will limit the mixing time, but if more mix is admitted balling up will start, especially when preparing a soft dough.

In the single-shaft Mixer the sense of rotation is of no importance, as the Mixer is completely symmetrical to the sense of rotation. With the double-shaft Mixer this is different, and experience has clearly shown that one sense of rotation is to be preferred; it is the one by which the mixing blades dive into the mix along the walls of the trough, and work out of the Mixer in the centre. This sense of rotation not only gives for better mixing, but also keeps the walls of the trough practically clean and free from dough accumulations.

The best material from which to construct the Mixer of a Continuous Extrusion Press is stainless steel, as this maintains a permanent polish which facilitates cleaning. The Mixers must be thoroughly cleaned whenever the Continuous Extrusion Press is stopped for more than a hour or two. If this is not done the dough will start to dry, and become sour. A Mixer that

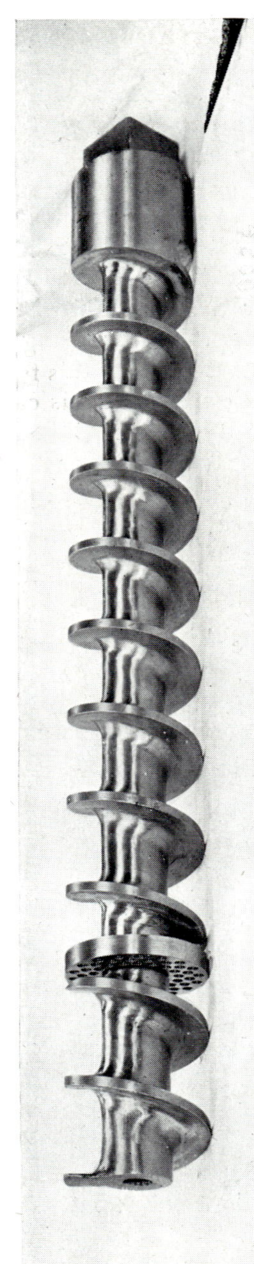

Fig. 28.—Extrusion Worm of the small Buhler Continuous Extrusion Press constructed in Stainless Steel incorporating welded kneading plate.

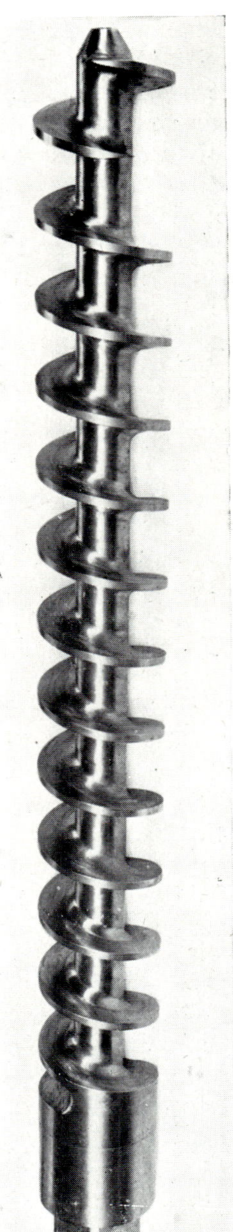

Fig. 29.—Stainless Steel Extrusion Worm without kneading plates.

will clean itself, is one of the major improvements yet to be achieved. All Mixers in operation to-day are difficult to empty and clean completely.

To ensure adequate protection of the operator, the Mixers of most Presses have a cover connected to the electrical system in such a way that opening of the cover automatically cuts off the power, making it impossible to re-start the motor before the cover is closed. The drives for the main Mixer and the feed Mixer should be separate, thus allowing the main Mixer to be stopped, emptied, and cleaned. During the time that the main Mixer is stopped, any mix removed from the walls or from the mixing blades may be fed into the feed Mixer and the Extrusion Press kept in operation, so that after cleaning the mixing trough, practically all the dough has passed into the Extrusion Worm.

The Extrusion Worm

The Extrusion Worm is the most vital part of the Continuous Extrusion Press. This worm kneads the mix, delivered by the Continuous Mixer, into an homogeneous dough, and builds up the pressure necessary to extrude the dough through the die. The construction and dimensions of Extrusion Worms vary considerably according to the type of Press being used. A standard form has not yet been established, some equipment manufacturers preferring a Worm with sharp edges, while others have the edges completely rounded off. The pitch of the Worm may be the same over the whole length or it may vary. The degree of pitch in some cases is regular; in others the Worm is divided into two or three sections with, at times, widely different pitches. The Worm is either continuous, or interrupted by kneading plates. Stainless steel and bronze are almost standard materials for the manufacture of these Extrusion Worms.

The extrusion pressure in Continuous Extrusion Presses is not as high as with Hydraulic Presses, as the dough made on a continuous machine is always softer, even though the same proportion of water has been used. The reason for this is that as soon as the dough has been kneaded it is extruded, and consequently has no time to dry or cool down as is the case with batch work. Such a dough is, therefore, more plastic, and easier to extrude. Pressures of about 1,500 lb. per sq. in. are average,

F

and seldom go beyond the 2,000 lb. mark. This latter pressure is only obtained where exceptionally dry and hard dough is being extruded.

As a rule the pressure built up by the Extrusion Worm is not constant. When the Press is started pressure rapidly reaches a peak, and then drops slowly and steadily down to the standard working level, which is reached only when the Press and the dough have attained a constant temperature. In most cases it will take a few hours for the pressure to come down to its final value. This is a big point in favour of running Continuous Extrusion Presses for 24 hours, whenever this is possible.

According to the type of Press, the diameter of the Worm may vary from 5 in. to 8 in. diameter, which means a total pressure of 15 to 40 tons on the thrust bearing. Heavy-type bearings must, therefore, be provided. The speed of the Worm is between 15 and 30 r.p.m. The lower speeds are generally used with large diameter Worms, while the higher speeds are more suitable for use with Worms of smaller diameter.

The volumetric efficiency of the Extrusion Worm is rather low and seldoms attains 30 per cent, leaving plenty of room for further improvement. The Extrusion Worm runs in a water jacketed cylinder made of special fine grain cast iron, and is often fitted with a bronze or stainless steel sleeve. Special care must be given to the choice of metal for the cylinder walls and the Extrusion Worm. These have to work together without lubrication, often for 24 hours a day 30 days a month.

In most Continuous Extrusion Presses the Worm "floats" inside the cylinder, being connected to the drive by means of a simple clutch. It is the pressure of the dough around the Worm that keeps it central and off the cylinder walls. To ensure the highest possibly efficiency the clearance between the Worm and the wall of the cylinder must be very small, and should not exceed about $\frac{2}{100}$ in. This clearance increases with time as the cylinder and Worm become worn, and a corresponding decrease in output will be noted. When the wear has attained $\frac{1}{10}$ in. or more, the loss of output of the Extrusion Worm becomes so large that it is advisable to equalize the bore of the cylinder in a lathe or with a special reamer. The diameter of the Worm may be increased by building up, and grinding to fit the new diameter of the cylinder. When a Press is used in a normal manner, cylinder and Worm should not require adjustment under about ten years. The Worm should never be allowed to rotate in an empty cylinder for any length of time as this will cause undue wear on the cylinder, and the wear which takes place will be uneven.

Kneading Plates

Some of the older types of Continuous Extrusion Presses have kneading plates fixed to the Worm, and rotating with it. Such kneading plates are particularly necessary on Presses with a small or inadequate Mixer. If the mix of Semolina and water has not been properly prepared in the Mixer, extra kneading is necessary and this is achieved by kneading plates.

Kneading must not be exaggerated, because this is detrimental to the quality of the gluten (*see page* 32). With the latest type of Extrusion Presses kneading plates are not used on the Worm. If kneading plates are required, one should be fitted into a recess at the head of the cylinder and kept in position by the cylinder head, and another arranged above the die. Both are easily removable, which makes it possible to adjust the amount of kneading required. The size, shape and number of kneading plates vary considerably according to the Extrusion Press under consideration, no standard construction having yet been evolved. The same may be said of the cylinder head.

The Cylinder Head

The cylinder head must be heated before the Press is started in order to ensure the correct temperature of the dough right from the beginning. After the Press has been working for about one hour, the heat may be reduced or completely shut off. With the exception of a Press with a vertical cylinder, the cylinder head diverts the horizontal flow of the dough to the vertical. It also carries the die, the initial ventilation system and the cutting knife.

A great many different constructions for cylinder heads have been made available, the general aim being to make the changing of the die as simple as possible, to get an even flow

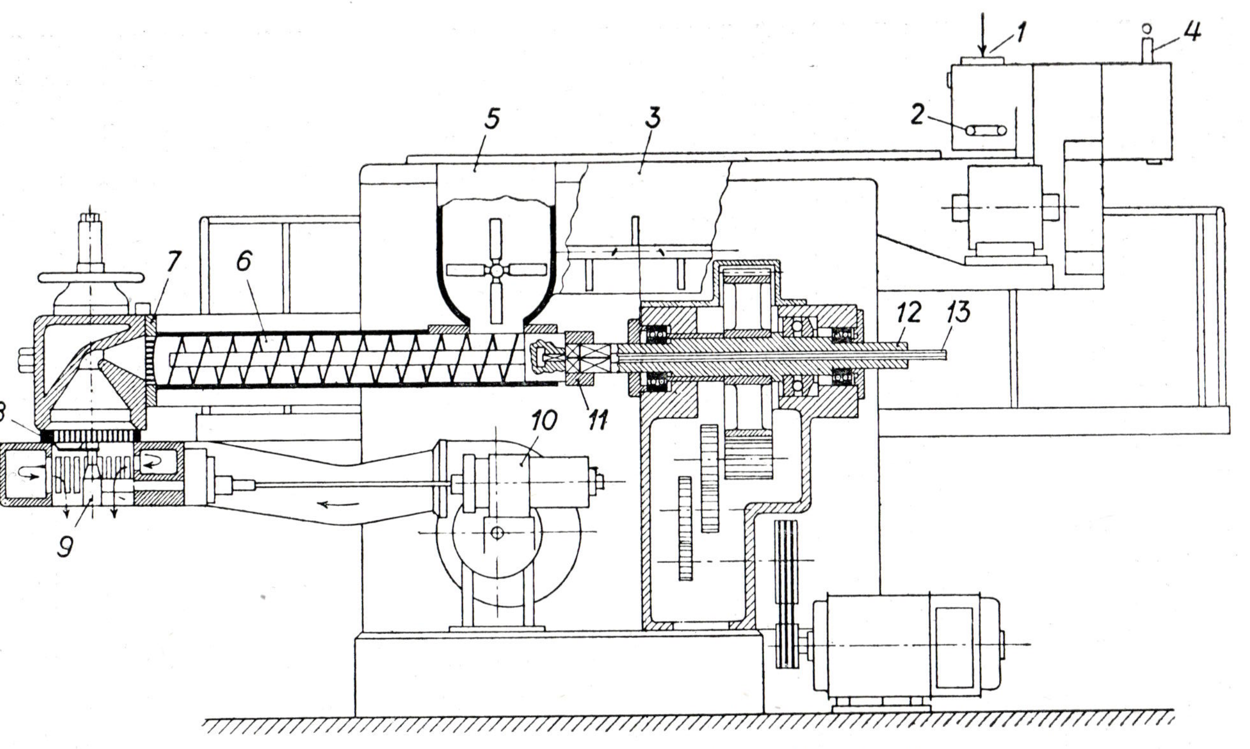

Fig. 30.—Cross Section of a Buhler Continuous Extrusion Press.

Fig. 31.—Die and Die Holder made by Officine Verrina.

of dough through the die, a regular distribution of air for the first ventilation and a handy means of positioning the Cutter. The cylinder head has to stand up to the heavy pressure of the dough, and must be built accordingly. As the temperature plays an important part in the flow of the dough, many cylinder heads are jacketed and provided with steam or electric heating. The illustration on page 85 clearly shows the space which is normally filled with water, oil or any other non-volatile fluid. This fluid can be heated by an electric coil. It is essential to have the temperature of the cylinder head and the

---

KEY TO FIG. 30.

1. Semolina Inlet.
2. Driving Belt for Semolina.
3. Mixer.
4. Dosing System for Water.
5. Feed Mixer.
6. Extrusion Worm.
7. Kneading Plate.
8. Die.
9. Cutter.
10. Cutter Motor and Continuous Variator.
11. Clutch.
12. Main Shaft.
13. Spindle used to remove Extrusion Worm.

cylinder properly balanced, as this has a most important bearing on the flow of the dough.

As a rule the cylinder head generally carries the die holder, which can be pulled up against the machined surface of the cylinder head. The die is held between the cylinder head and the die holder under heavy pressure, obtained by tightening the screws with which the die holder is fixed. These screws are tightened by using large hand-wheels or heavy spanners. A dough-tight fit of the die is facilitated by the use of a bronze sealing ring inserted between the die and the cylinder head. The sealing ring, the surface of the die, and the cylinder head upon which it rests, must always be kept perfectly clean if the sealing ring is to be effective. Particular care must be taken to raise the die holder in such a way that an even pressure is exerted over the whole surface of the die. If this is not done it is possible that the sealing ring will burst with the pressure of the dough.

To ensure correct setting of the die holder, some manufacturers are using a Worm and Wheel gear or a built-in motor. These ensure that the die and sealing ring are correctly

Fig. 32(a).—Buhler Cutter for short cut Macaroni Products with two cutting arms.

positioned. Certain Extrusion Presses are provided with a rotatable die holder, which can rotate round one of the spindles by which the die is tightened against the cylinder head. In this event it is sufficient only to lower the die holder far enough to enable the die to be swung out of position. Without the rotatable die holder, the die holder must be screwed down until it is possible to lift the die out of the recess in which it is seated.

Fig. 32(*b*).—Cutter of the Buhler Continuous Extrusion Press showing method of attachment.

Cutters for Short Cut Macaroni Products

Short cut Macaroni Products are produced by running a knife over the surface of the die as the dough is extruded. If the speed of the knife and the extrusion speed of the Macaroni Products are suitably combined, the extruded product may be cut to any length between $\frac{1}{50}$ in. and 2 in. The Cutter consists of one or more arms fitted to a rotating shaft, each arm being fitted with an exchangeable well-sharpened blade that runs flush with the die, cutting the Macaroni Product as it is extruded. In order to ensure a clean cut the blades must run on the die with only light pressure; this is usually obtained by having the arms spring loaded. Whenever possible each arm should have its own spring, as this makes for easier adjustment.

The cutting blades must be re-sharpened at fairly frequent intervals, and it is desirable that they should be removed without recourse to tools. On the Buhler Press they are fitted to the shaft by a hand-operated set nut. When the blades have to

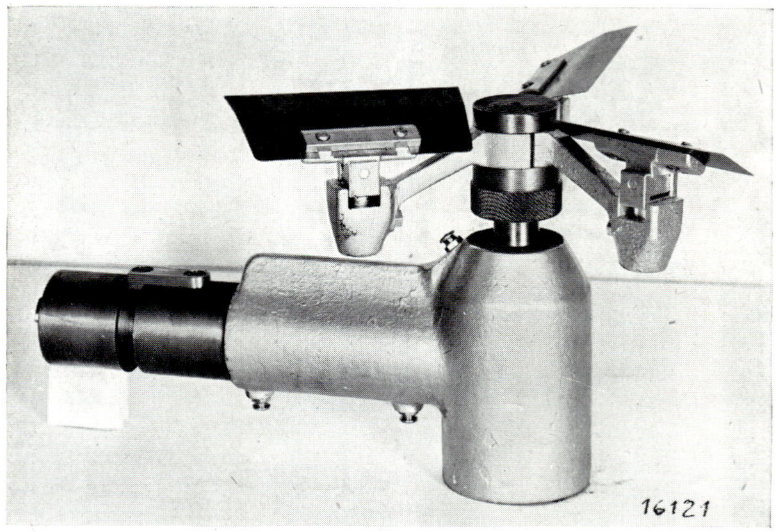

Fig. 32(c).—Cutter with three arms for Short Cut Macaroni Products.

be changed it is essential that such changes should be made as rapidly as possible, in order that the Press may be switched over from manufacturing long goods to short goods without stopping the Press for more than a very short time. This construction has now been adopted by many manufacturers of paste goods equipment.

The Cutters are usually driven by a small independent motor, thus making it possible to have a safety switch fitted to cut out the motor and prevent major damage should the knife run into a protruding pin on a die making hollow goods.

The power from the motor is transmitted to the Cutter through a continuous speed variator.

The speed variators as used on Hydraulic Presses working

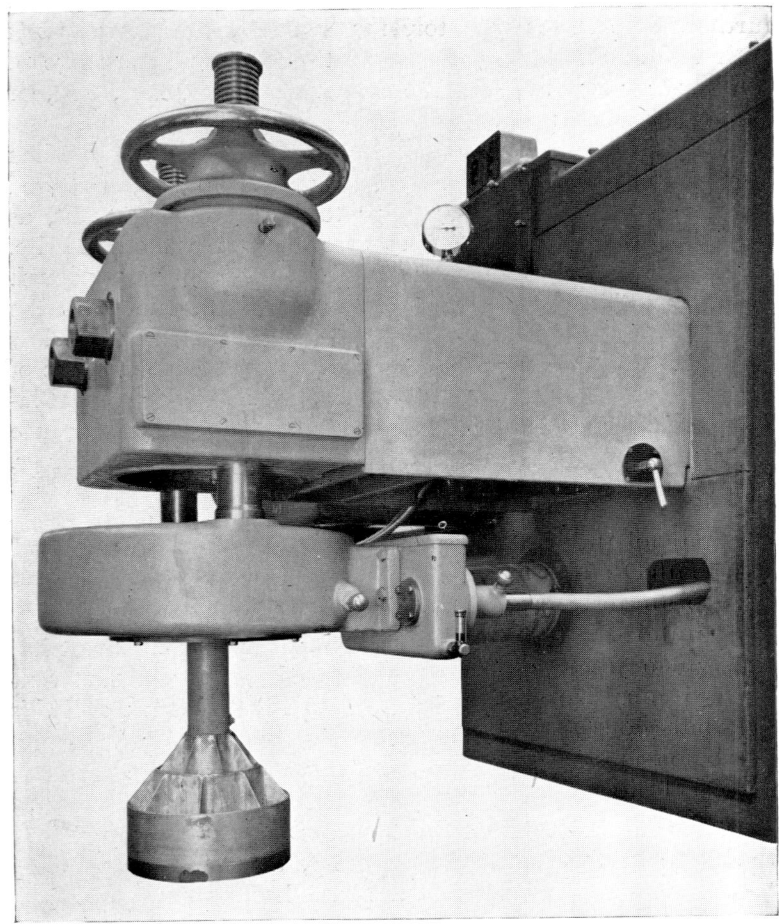

Fig. 33.—Close-up of Cutter on the Buhler Continuous Extrusion Press for cutting long goods.

with discs or conical belt drives, have generally been superseded by the well-known P.V. Drives, mechanical variators, such as the Arter Drive, and in some cases by Hydraulic Drives. The variation of speed must have a very wide range, about 1 : 100.

When using Cutters with from one to four arms, it is possible to cut down the range to be transmitted by the variator to 1 : 25, and by using a reduction gear-box with two outgoing shafts, the range of the variator can be reduced further. The Arter variator, for instance, uses a gear-box with two shafts having a speed ratio of 1 : 5. The range of the variator is 1 : 8, and the total range using one, two, or three knives is 1 : 120.

The ordinary Cutter will not work satisfactorily when producing short cut goods in fairly long lengths, scattered noodles, short cut Macaroni, or tubes with a slant cut, as the knife rotates too slowly to give a clean cut on the die. Before the cutting blade is clear of the extruding hole dough is already building up behind the blade, as the extrusion speed of the dough is too high in comparison with the low speed of the knife. Another difficulty is that a heavy mass of dough builds up before the knife and gets no proper ventilation, so that the strings of dough begin to stick and pack into large heaps that do not separate on the preliminary Drier, and therefore have to be rejected.

All these difficulties are overcome by using a special cutting device, illustrated in Fig. 33. As the strings of dough leave the die they are allowed to flow freely for about 25 in., they are then gathered in a ring with suitable divisions and cut by a knife running on the lower edge of the ring. This arrangement has two advantages, viz. the strings of dough get a good first ventilation as they flow from the die to the cutting ring, and this ventilation is sufficient to prevent them from sticking. Secondly, the comparatively slow moving knife being some distance from the die, does not interfere with the continuous flow of the dough from the die. The strings of dough actually rest on the knife at the moment of cutting, and being supported, take the form of a curve until the knife has passed. This makes it possible for the dough to flow evenly from the die independent of the position of the knife. The ring on which the strings of dough are cut may be flat, which will give a straight cut, or conical as shown in the illustration, producing the slant cut.

Another method of producing longer short cut Macaroni Products is to use a knife that does not run continuously over the face of the die at a constant speed, but is so arranged to run across the face of the die at a normal speed and then stop.

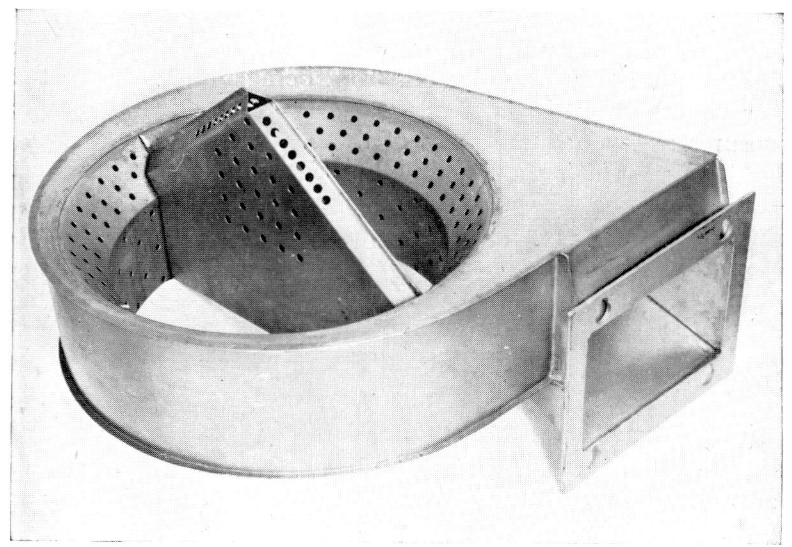

Fig. 34.—Ring-shaped canal which distributes air on the strings
of dough as they are extruded.

To do this it is necessary to manufacture the die so that there
are no extrusion holes on the part of the die on which the
knife will rest. The time during which the knife is at rest
may be longer than the time required for the knife to pass
over the face of the die, thus making it possible to leave sufficient
time between two cuts for the Macaroni Product to be extruded
to the required length, and yet have a cutting speed that will
ensure a clean cut. This type of Cutter is of necessity more
elaborate than the ordinary Cutters operating at a constant
speed and is not often used, as practically all short cut Macaroni
Products can be produced in a satisfactory way with a
continuously driven knife.

First ventilation is most important in order to obtain a
clean cut, and to avoid the strings of dough sticking together.
On all Hydraulic Presses and on most Continuous Extrusion
Presses the air for this first ventilation is distributed by a
ring-shaped canal arranged below the die holder. An alternative arrangement may be used whereby the die holder is
hollow, and distributes the air directly into the dough strings
as they leave the die. This construction keeps the die dry

and prevents the dough from sticking, thus ensuring even working of the Cutter. An easily interchangeable ring of wire mesh prevents short cut goods from being projected into the air chamber by the rotating Cutter, and at the same time ensures an even distribution of the air.

The ventilating air is usually delivered from a fan built into the frame of the Extrusion Press. A valve incorporated in the air duct regulates the quantity of air, and makes it possible to control the air to suit the goods being produced. Long Macaroni and long Spaghetti require a large amount of ventilation, while the smaller type of short cut goods will be scattered if exposed to a strong blast of air.

The Drive of the Continuous Extrusion Press

All Continuous Extrusion Presses are driven by electric motors complete with suitable reduction gear. The extrusion Worm, as we have seen, runs at a speed of approximately 20 r.p.m., and requires a heavy torque. A very sturdily built reduction gear is required to transform the high speed low torque power of the electric motor into the low speed high torque power, necessary to drive the extrusion Worm against the resistance of the tough dough under high pressure inside the cylinder.

Modern Continuous Extrusion Presses have separate motors for the various drives. It is usual to have a motor to drive the feeding system and the main Mixer, and a separate motor for the feed Mixer where used. A separate motor is used for each the Extrusion Worm, Cutter, and for the Fan. The electrical equipment of these motors, fuses, switches and cut-offs, should be located in a central distributing panel, and the motors controlled by push-button starters mounted at suitable points on the machine.

CHAPTER VI

SOME TYPICAL CONTINUOUS EXTRUSION PRESSES

THE Braibanti Continuous Extrusion Press made by Braibanti, of Italy, and the Buhler Continuous Extrusion Press made by Buhler Brothers, of Switzerland, were the first Continuous Presses available in large numbers to Macaroni manufacturers. The older Tabucchi Press was made in very small numbers, and the machine was not put on the market for sale generally.

BRAIBANTI

The Braibanti Press is characterized by its combination of horizontal mixer and vertical extrusion worm, together with a high two-legged frame, which has made it possible to fit a Pre-Drier into the Press. This general arrangement has been maintained in its main outline to the present day.

BUHLER

The Buhler Continuous Extrusion Press was first put on the market in 1934. It has since been steadily developed and strengthened, and is now more powerful and compact. The illustration on page 94 shows the Buhler Press, Type T.P.J. The two Semolina feeding belts and the hand-wheels for setting the quantity of Semolina passing to the Press, the separate motor for the main Mixer, the short goods Cutter and the Fan can all be clearly seen. The switches for the heating unit which is built into the cylinder head are also clearly visible. The four hand-wheels arranged vertically one above the other are, from top to bottom:

(1) Control valve between the Feed Mixer and the cylinder;
(2) To disengage the clutch driving the extrusion worm, and to extrude the worm by running the main motor;
(3) Regulator for short goods Cutter; and
(4) Air control.

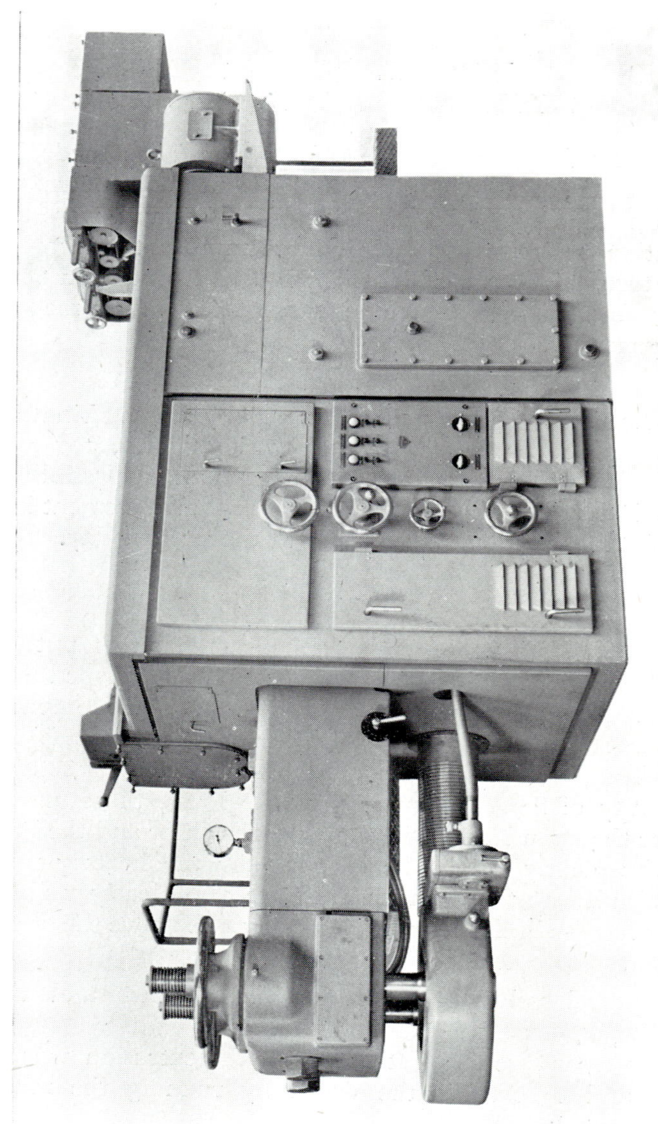

Fig. 35.—Buhler Continuous Extrusion Press, type T.P.J.

The circular thermometer indicates the temperature of the cylinder. The die holder, the tube carrying the air into the die holder, and the flexible shaft for the Cutter drive, are also clearly visible in this illustration.

The illustration shows the Buhler small Continuous

Fig. 36.—Buhler Small Continuous Extrusion Press.

Extrusion Press with an hourly output of about 2 cwt. This Press has been made for countries that have small Macaroni manufacturing plants. It is also used by larger manufacturers to handle trimmings, and for the manufacture of certain specialities. This machine has been put forward for the production of a sheet of dough, which is sent to a Dough

Breaker and a Stamping Machine for producing "Pasta Bologna" (or bows) in a continuous operation.

A similar arrangement using a Twisting Machine will produce curls.

CLERMONT

The Clermont Continuous Extrusion Press, made by the Clermont Machine Corp. Inc., of Brooklyn, New York, is rather different from the two machines previously mentioned, the pressure in this Press being built up by rolls as on the old Tabucchi Press. Semolina and water are fed into a continuous Mixer, and the mix delivered into the nip of a pair of

Fig. 37.—Consolidated Continuous Extrusion Press combining Long Goods Spreader.

rolls where a sheet of dough is formed. This dough then passes to a second pair of rolls where it is further kneaded and forced into a compression chamber, which carries the die through which the dough is extruded. Scrapers bearing against the rolls keep them clean, and ensure that all the dough goes into the compression chamber.

CONSOLIDATED

One of the Consolidated Extrusion Presses made by the Consolidated Macaroni Machine Corp., of Brooklyn, New York, was an Hydraulic Press combined with a long goods

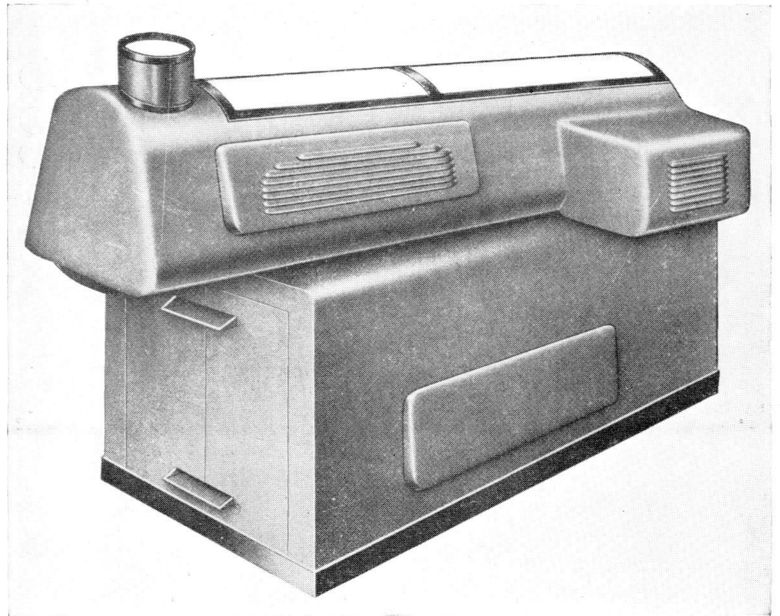

Fig. 38.—Continuous Extrusion Press made by Premoli & Baudino, Milan.

Spreader. This has now been replaced by a Continuous Extrusion Press combined with a Spreader for long Macaroni Products. Further details of this construction will be given later in this chapter, when dealing with the Automatic Spreader for long Macaroni Products. Another Continuous Extrusion Press made

G

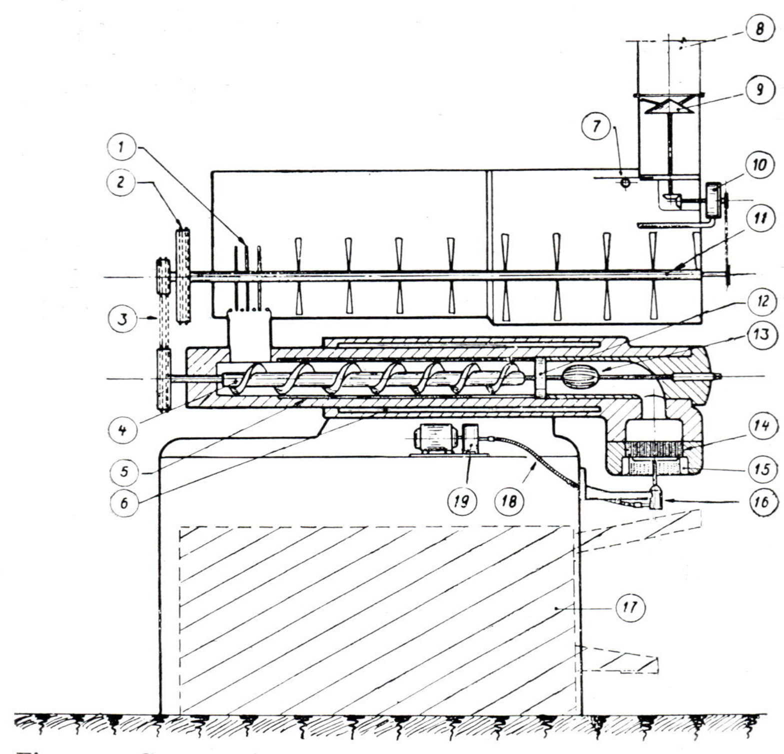

Fig. 39.—Cross section of the Continuous Extrusion Press made
by Premoli & Baudino, Milan.

KEY

1. Cutters feeding the mix into
   the Worm.
2 & 3. Driers.
4. Extrusion Worm.
5. Cylinder.
6. Water Jacket.
7. Semolina Feed.
8. Inlet for Semolina.
9. Agitator ensuring regular
   flow of Semolina.
10. Water Feed.
11. Mixing Shaft.
12. Kneading Plate.
13. Dough Distributor.
14. Die.
15. Air Channel.
16. Cutter.
17. Exit of Pre-Drier.
18. Flexible Shaft.
19. Variable Drive for Cutter.

by Consolidated and arranged for short cut Macaroni Products is combined with a Pneumatic Conveyor for the short goods.

FATI

The Fati Continuous Extrusion Press, made by Premoli & Baudino, of Milan, is remarkable for its general appearance and

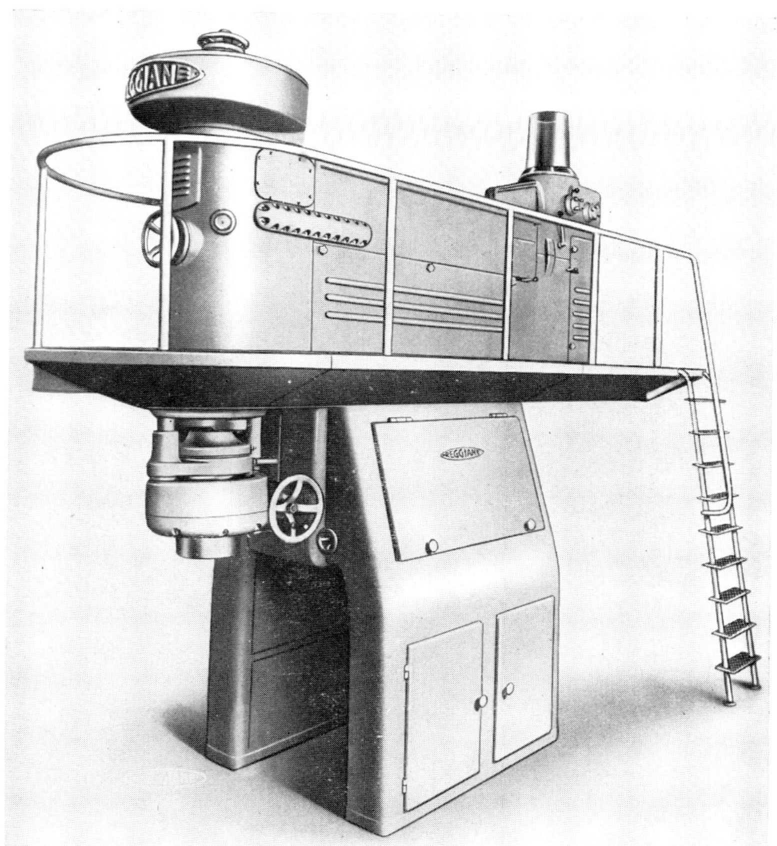

Fig. 40.—"Reggiane" Continuous Extrusion Press.

smooth outline. The cross-section shown on page 98 shows very clearly the general arrangement, which with certain modifications is to be found in practically all Continuous Extrusion Presses using a Worm to build up the necessary pressure.

MORIONDO

The Moriondo Continuous Extrusion Press, built by
Moriondo & Co., of Milan, is one of the few Extrusion Presses
used in the manufacture of Macaroni Products with a grooved
bronze lining in the cylinder. The helical grooves are provided with a view to assisting the kneading of the dough.
However, this construction has the obvious drawback of
making the cleaning of the cylinder more difficult.

REGGIANE

The "Reggiane" Continuous Extrusion Press, built by the

Fig. 41.—Continuous Extrusion Press built by Stige S.P.A., Genoa.

Officine Meccaniche Italiane S.A., of Italy, is a two-legged construction and accommodates a pre-Drier. This machine includes some very notable features, being fitted with a combined Semolina and water feed, and a special cylinder head construction facilitating changing of the die. The Mixer is jacketed, making it possible to regulate the temperature of the mix, before it goes to the extrusion Worm. This Extrusion Press is also supplied with a Trim Shredder, which is fitted on the Mixer and driven by a small belt. The trimmings are put into the hopper, and extruded through a small die by an extrusion Worm located in the bottom of the hopper. With this Trim Shredder trimmings are distributed regularly into

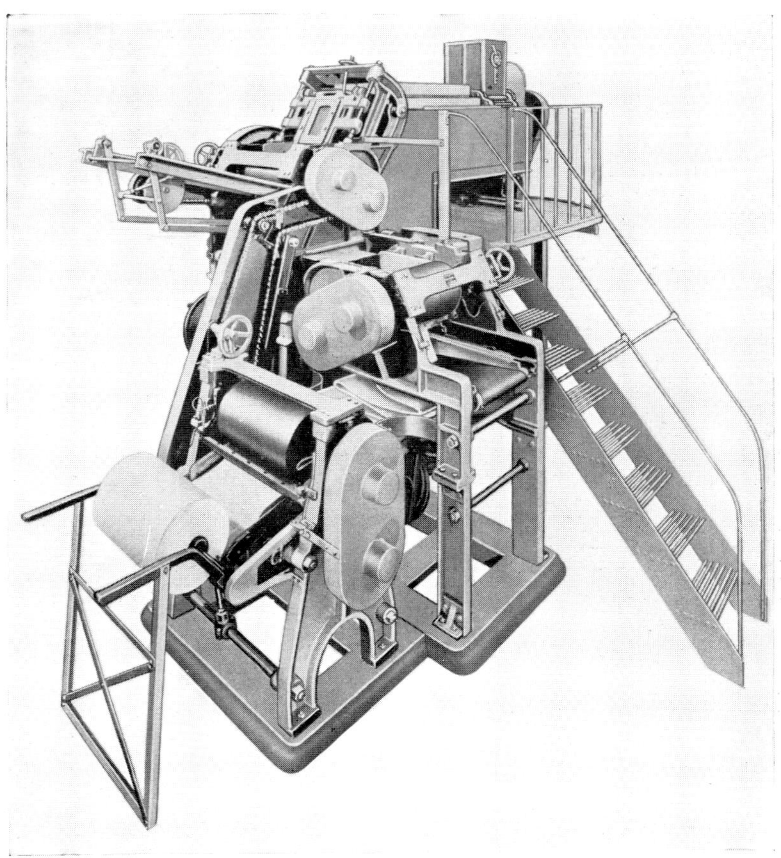

Fig. 42.—Clermont Automatic Sheet Forming Machine.

the mix, and this considerably helps to ensure the production of goods of uniform quality without discarding the trimmings.

Unica Damiano

The Unica Damiano built by Stige S.P.A., of Genoa, is a Continuous Extrusion Press using a double shaft Mixer. One main motor drives the Feed, the Mixer and the Worm. The built-in pre-Drier has three different speeds, the low speed giving the short cut goods a pre-drying time of about five minutes.

ROLLED MACARONI PRODUCTS

Clermont Automatic Sheet Forming Machine

The most important Continuous Extrusion Press for the production of rolled and cut Macaroni Products is the Clermont Automatic Sheet Forming Machine.

The operation of this machine is as follows: Flour and water are fed continuously into a continuous Mixer exactly like any other Continuous Extrusion Press. The mix is then forced into the nip of a pair of rolls and delivered as a sheet of dough to a criss-crossing device, which, after the sheet has been folded, feeds the dough into a second pair of rolls mounted at right-angles to the first pair. A second criss-crossing device feeds the sheet to the third pair of rolls, the axis of which is at right-angles to the axis of the second pair of rolls. The dough is then delivered by this third pair of rolls as a finished sheet, ready to go to the Noodle Cutter, or to be wound on a wooden spool for subsequent use on a Noodle Cutter or Stamping Machine. A combination of Clermont Sheet Forming Machine, Noodle Cutter and Continuous Noodle Drier has been arranged which makes the most powerful and up-to-date unit for the production of rolled Noodles, having an output of up to 1,600 lb. per hour.

Buhler Sheet Forming Device

By using a special die any Continuous Extrusion Press can be made to extrude a sheet of dough. The first dies of this type made by Buhler in 1935 used a slot, and extruded a sheet of dough that was a little narrower than the diameter of the die. For large productions this was insufficient, and at

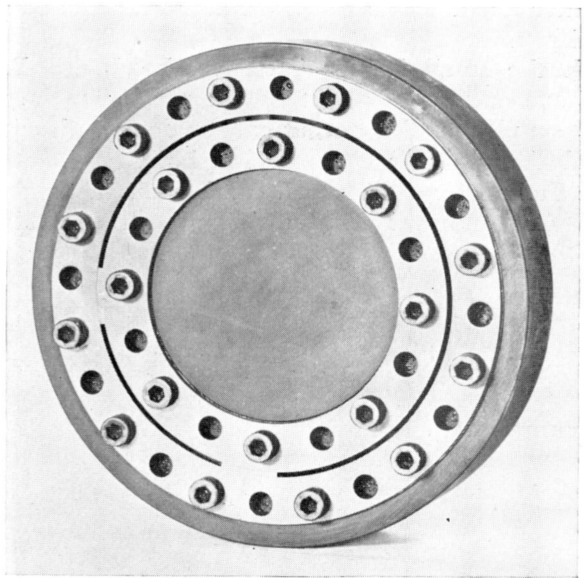

Fig. 43.—Buhler Die with circular slot for producing a sheet of dough. Width and thickness of
the sheet can be regulated.

a later date a die was made with a circular slot. This made
it possible to extrude a sheet of dough up to 30 in. wide,
which was more than sufficient for use with any standard
Noodle Cutter.

To obtain a Noodle with the characteristic appearance
and cooking qualities of the rolled Noodle, kneading of the
dough on the Continuous Extrusion Press is reduced to the
minimum necessary to produce a consistent sheet, this sheet
of dough being fed continuously over two pairs of Calibrating
Rolls and then to a Noodle Cutter. This arrangement produces
a Noodle of perfect texture, and with all the qualities of a
rolled Noodle. The output is fairly high, approximately
1,200 lb. per hour, and is obtained by using a standard Continuous Extrusion Press and fitting a suitable die. The same
group of machines can be used for the production of stamped
goods, such as "bows". There has been difficulty in syn-
chronizing the output of the large Buhler Continuous Extrusion
Press with standard Stamping Machines, as the output of

these latter machines is so much lower than the output of a
Buhler Press.

With the small Buhler Press or the Micro Braibanti,
which have outputs of about 2 cwt. per hour, the problem
is much simpler, as this output can be dealt with easily on a
standard Stamping or Twisting Machine.

The Italian firm of N. &. V. Pavan, of Venice, have
built a Continuous Extrusion Press with a double head

Fig. 44.—Spreader for Spaghetti used with a
Hydraulic Press built by Werner & Pfleiderer.

accommodating two dies, thereby making it possible to
extrude two sheets of dough simultaneously feeding two
Stamping Machines. In this case the total capacity of the
large Continuous Extrusion Press can be utilized for the
production of rolled Macaroni Products, but instances where

this is really economical are rare. Other firms like Barducci and Cressoni & Bossi are also using two heads on one Press, but only for the production of standard Macaroni Products.

Spreaders for Long Macaroni Products

I have already stated in a previous chapter (page 49) that it is necessary to put long Macaroni Products on sticks before they can be dried. This work not only requires a great deal of labour when done by hand, on an average one man and two girls are needed for the output of a modern Continuous Extrusion Press, but it is also objectionable from a hygienic point of view, as it involves considerable handling of the fresh long goods.

Various devices have been built during the past few years to reduce this handling to a minimum, and one of the first successful machines was the Spreader built by Werner & Pfleiderer. This Spreader uses special short sticks, and the drying cabinets have to be altered to accommodate these sticks. The Spreader works with all types of Vertical Presses. Standard dies were used, and as the Presss was not modified and could also be used for short goods, much was expected of the Werner & Pfleiderer device, but experience showed that the necessity of utilizing special short sticks resulted in increased labour, and the considerable amount of trimmings obtained prevented this first Spreader from gaining any great popularity. This Spreader was introduced before Continuous Extrusion Presses came into general use, and as the demand for such a machine was not extensive, very little development work was carried out on this system.

An entirely different type of Spreader was developed by the Mécanique Méridionale. Working in conjunction with Belt Conveyors this Spreader is a semi-automatic machine. Sticks are introduced and taken one by one, and the Cutters operated by hand. As this machine requires a fair amount of labour and production is somewhat limited, it has not been brought into general use.

A really efficient Spreader for long Macaroni Products was manufactured by Buhler in the Spring of 1939. This Spreader may be adjusted to use existing sticks of any length between 3 ft. and 5 ft., and, therefore, no modification to

Fig. 45.—Buhler Spreader for Long Macaroni Products combined
with a Continuous Extrusion Press.

existing Driers was required. Built for use with a Continuous
Extrusion Press, this Spreader was very quickly accepted by
the majority of manufacturers of long Macaroni Products,
and proved to be one of the most hygienic and labour-saving
devices offered to the Macaroni industry. The illustration
above shows such a Spreader combined with a Continuous
Extrusion Press, the standard Press head having been replaced
by a special head. This carries the Spreader arm in which is
positioned the special die, and the dough coming from the
Press flows through the arm and is extruded through the die.
In the first models set-screws were provided to regulate the

flow of the dough from the arms to the individual dies. In later models the set-screws have been replaced by thermostatic control of the temperature of the distributing arm. The extrusion holes in the dies are arranged to produce a regular row of long goods, in which the strings of dough already have the position they should occupy on the sticks. The length of the row corresponds to the length of the sticks.

The empty sticks are filled into a magazine on the front side of the Spreader, a mechanical device putting them one by one into carriers fixed at regular intervals on a chain. The carriers are fixed to the chain by pins and run on needle bearings. Their own weight assisted by guides keeps them in a vertical position even when the chain is running over a sprocket. After the sticks have fallen into the carriers they are carried behind the screen formed by the strings of dough, and when the strings have been extruded to the required length the advancing sticks automatically pick them up. The strings of dough now hang freely over the sticks on one side, and form a wave on the other side where they are still connected to the die. When this wave has acquired the necessary length a knife cuts all the strings of dough, and the long Macaroni Products hang on both sides of the stick. The stick is then carried by the chain to a second knife, which cuts the irregular strings of dough to a prescribed length. This knife can be adjusted on a rail, so that it will cut the long goods to any required length. The trimmings fall on to a Belt Conveyor, which carries them to a Trim Shredder.

In the Shredder the trimmings are shredded into small pieces having a length of less than 1 in. They are then conveyed into the Mixer of the Continuous Extrusion Press by air pressure produced by a Fan which forms part of the Trim Shredder, thus the trimmings are returned to the Mixer within a few seconds after they have been produced. The trimmings have had no chance to dry and are perfectly fresh, and they are thus incorporated into the dough without any disadvantage. This makes it possible to turn the total amount of Semolina into first-class long Macaroni Products.

As with the Continuous Extrusion Press, the Spreader is driven by built-in motors, controlled from an electric panel.

This Trim Shredder by Buhler is also available as an independent unit, and may be used wherever trimmings are produced. Contrary to an opinion which has often been expressed, the trimmings are not dried in the Pneumatic Conveyor. The time they are in the pipe of the Conveyor exposed to the air blast, seldom exceeds two seconds, and this time is too short to produce any noticeable loss of moisture.

Reverting to the Automatic Spreader, the movement of the chain and the first knife are delicately synchronized. The Spreader is driven by a variable speed drive, so that the speed of the Spreader can be adjusted to the extrusion speed of the goods being produced. The sticks filled with long goods are deposited on a slow moving chain, acting as a stock chain, and are taken from this by hand as required, to be dried in any suitable long goods Drier.

On an average sticks of a little over 3 ft. in length can be filled with about 500 strings of Spaghetti of average diameter, but this number is quite insufficient to absorb the normal output of a Continuous Extrusion Press. The output of such a Press can be computed quite easily by multiplying the number of holes in the die, the weight of the extruded product per unit of length, and the extrusion speed. As the weight is governed by the type of long goods being produced, the output depends mainly on the number of holes and the extrusion speed. On a Spreader working with a Continuous Extrusion Press the speed for Spaghetti should not exceed about 6 ft. per second, if the goods are not to be unduly rough. This means that with sticks of about 3 ft. in length only about 3 cwt. can be spread per hour. As most Continuous Extrusion Presses will handle twice this quantity, all Spreaders have to be built to handle two sticks at a time. On the Spreader illustrated on page 106, the two sticks are handled one behind the other. Two sets of holes in the die produce two screens of long goods one behind the other, each section going to a separate stick. Similar Spreaders have been built by Consolidated.

The sticks on these Spreaders are all delivered on one line, and this has suggested the idea of carrying the sticks automatically into a Continuous pre-Drier, a construction developed by both Consolidated and Buhler, or to a Continuous Drier in which they are dried ready for packing, a construction marketed by Buhler.

A chainless Spreader has been built by Officine Meccaniche

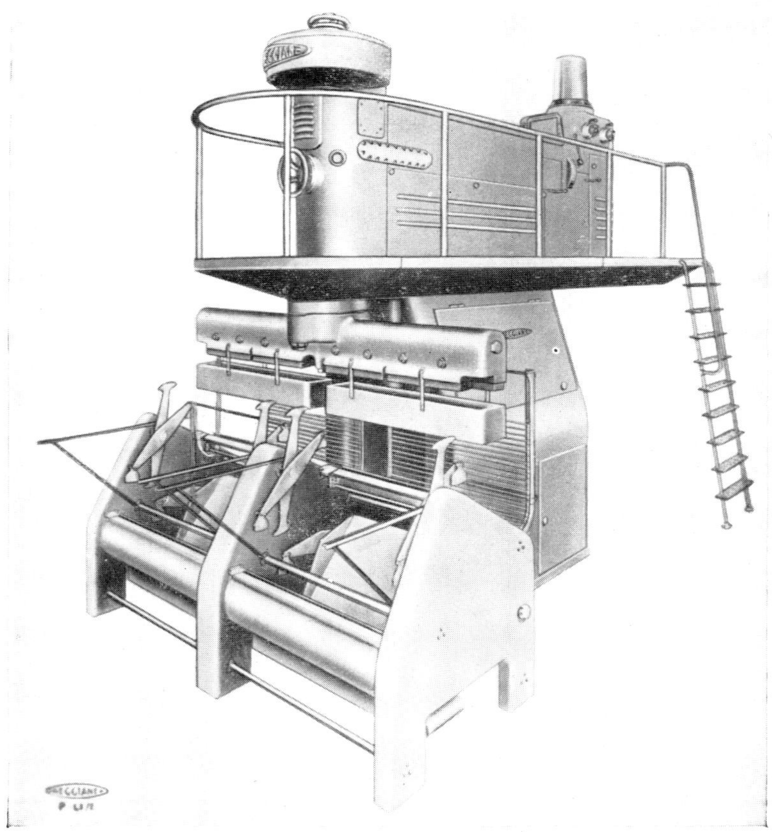

Fig. 46.—"Reggiane" Chainless Spreader for solid goods.

Italiane, S.A. This is a double Spreader, and, therefore, cannot be used in conjunction with a Continuous pre-Drier or a Continuous Drier.

Spreaders that are expected to handle hollow goods, should cut the Macaroni on the die. If this is not done a certain proportion of Macaroni will always be crushed by the knife, and, as this will stop the air from flowing into the Macaroni, the corresponding strings of dough will become flat. The Buhler and the Consolidated Spreaders both cut the dough on the die, and can be used for both solid and hollow goods. The "Reggiane" Spreaders do not cut on the die, and therefore should be used only for solid goods.

Fig. 47(*a*).—Inlet side of Round Macaroni Die.

Fig. 47(*b*).—Extrusion side of Round Macaroni Die.

Fig. 48(*a*).—Inlet side of square Macaroni Die.

Spreaders are reliable, efficient machines, but require to be fed with reasonably straight sticks of regular length. Most of the trouble experienced with these machines is caused by the use of unsuitable sticks. For this reason sticks of stainless steel made to an exact specification, are used and recommended by Buhler for use with the Spreader built into the Buhler Continuous Drier.

Dies

All extruded Macaroni Products have to pass through a Die, which is one of the most important items of all Extrusion Presses. Generally speaking, Dies are manufactured from bronze. An average bronze of good hardness and tensile strength, and as homogeneous as possible must be chosen. Bronze is easy to machine, acquiring a high polish, and has a good resistance against the corrosive effects of dough and water. Dies in stainless steel have been used by some large manufacturers, but these are more expensive than bronze, mainly due to the fact that stainless steel is more difficult and expensive to machine. Stainless steel Dies have the advantage of retaining their polish better than any other type of Die, and can, therefore, be used for a long period before requiring repolishing. Aluminium has also been used but as this is rather soft, the holes lose their polish more quickly than bronze or stainless steel, and consequently the goods produced through aluminium Dies tend to become rough.

Most Dies have a circular formation, although some are square. The same type of Die is used on both Hydraulic and

Fig. 48(*b*).—Extrusion side of square Macaroni Die.

Continuous Extrusion Presses, the diameter of a Die varying according to the size of the Press. The current sizes range between 8 in. and 14 in. The thickness of the Die varies between $1\frac{1}{2}$ in. and $2\frac{1}{2}$ in., and is dependent on the diameter, and the pressure of the dough being extruded from the Press.

For Automatic Spreaders long narrow Dies are now in general use. The illustration on page 114 shows a Die from a Buhler Spreader utilizing two sticks one behind the other. The double row of holes corresponding to the two sticks are plainly visible. Large diameter Dies must be thick if they are not to be distorted by the pressure of the dough. Thick Dies require extra pressure to extrude the dough through the long hole, and consequently reduce the output. To obviate these drawbacks a central spindle has been used especially on Hydraulic Presses, which, after being brought up against the centre of the Die, prevents the deflection of the Die. This spindle hinders the flow of the Macaroni Products, and must be reset each time the Die is changed.

A construction has been developed for Continuous Extrusion Presses which rests on the rim of the Die and supports the centre. This construction does not interfere with the flow of the extruded goods, and makes it possible to use Dies of large diameter and moderate thickness. The shape of the support may be chosen to regulate the flow of the dough, i.e. so as to obtain short cut Macaroni Products of even length.

A good Die should have as many holes as are compatible with its strength, and such a Die will yield a maximum output. A Die with a reduced number of holes will be cheaper to make, but due to the smaller output is more expensive in the long run.

The holes of a Die have a fairly long cylindrical part of comparatively large diameter ending in a short section, which is shaped to give the Macaroni Product its distinctive form. Dies for solid goods such as Spaghetti, for instance, are fairly simple to manufacture. They are more complicated, however, when the production of hollow goods are required, as here it is necessary to introduce a pin to provide the hole in the hollow goods. These pins are provided with wings to support and retain them in position. The wings split the dough, but the high pressure behind the dough immediately closes these splits, and as it passes the last part of the hole the pin leaves an uninterrupted annular path for the dough. The pins must be exactly centred if straight Macaroni of uniform thickness is to be produced. If the pins are slightly eccentric the dough will flow faster on the side where the clearance is greater, and curved Elbows will be produced. As Elbows are cut on the

H

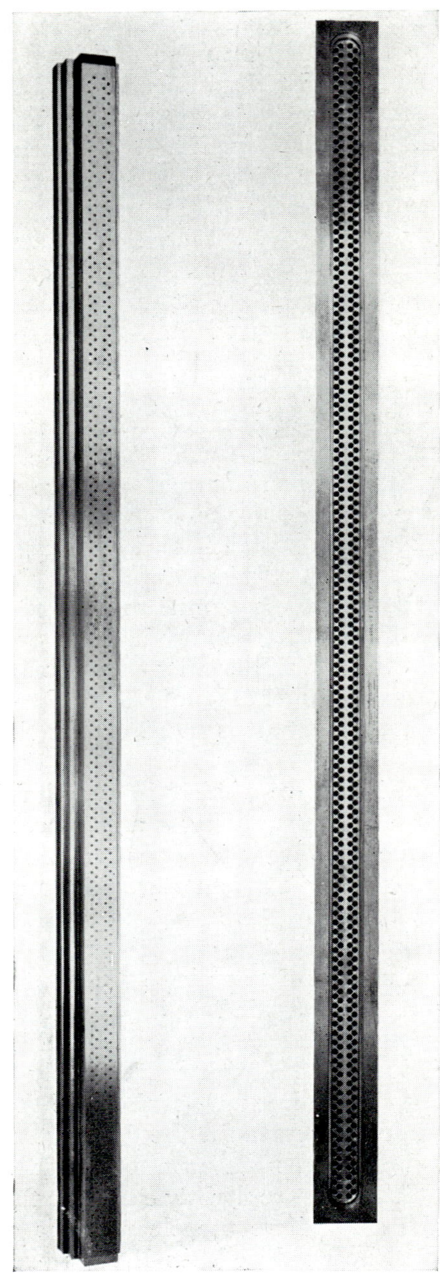

Fig. 49.—Two views of a Die for Mechanical Spreader.

Die by a rotating knife, care must be taken to ensure that none of the pins protrude through the Die. Even if the pin protrudes for only a fraction of an inch, this will cause damage to the rotating knife.

When making Dies it is essential to bear in mind that with a Continuous Extrusion Press, dried Macaroni Products will be about 10 per cent smaller than the diameter of the hole in the Die. This shrinkage is reduced to about 8 per cent on Hydraulic Presses, as with these machines it is customary to use a harder dough.

Extruded Noodles may be produced on a Die in exactly the same manner as Spaghetti, but instead of utilizing a round hole the Die is provided with a number of slots. Dies for Shells and similar products are more elaborate. For these products the hole into which the dough is forced is very large compared with the extrusion section, and such Dies have a much smaller output. For solid goods the Dies may often be replaced by a die plate. This applies to Noodles, Spaghetti, and more particularly, Vermicelli. Die plates have the advantage of being cheap, and of working effectively with only a moderate pressure. They are not self-supporting, and can be used only when combined with a die support. The die support makes it impossible to use a knife flush with the Die. In certain cases a Die with inserts can be used.

The products that can be extruded through a Die are of remarkable variety. The Die catalogue of Ricciarelli Pistoia gives 802 different shapes. A large number of these shapes only vary in some small dimension, but even so the variety of Dies is extensive, and there is no doubt that Macaroni Product manufacturers will be well advised to select only a restricted collection of shapes.

Dies must always be kept in perfect order. When a Die has been in use for a certain time the polished surfaces of the holes becomes rough, and as soon as this is apparent the Die should be returned to the makers to be repolished.

Die Washing Machines

Smooth and perfectly regular Macaroni Products can only be produced with perfectly clean Dies. Any hard impurities contained in the Semolina or small pieces of dried dough have a tendency to stick in the small space between the pin and the wall of the hole in the Die, or in the small holes when extruding thin solid goods. Such impurities will cut the wall of long

Fig. 50.—Buhler Die Washing Machine for round and long dies.

hollow goods, and solid goods will extrude irregularly and often become curled.

Therefore, it is necessary to thoroughly clean the Dies from time to time. This can be done on a Die Washing Machine, where the Dies are cleaned by a fine jet of water under high pressure. No attempt should be made to clean the Die by using metal scrapers, as these will scratch the polished surface of the holes and spoil them. Dough should never be left in the Die to dry, and if the Die cannot be cleaned immediately after having been taken down, it should be put into clear running water to soak. It will take anything from half an hour to two hours to clean the Die completely in a Die Washing Machine. The time, however, depends upon the state of the Die, i.e. softness of the dough in the holes, and the type of Die Washing Machine used.

All Die Washing Machines consist essentially of a pump, delivering high-pressure water through jets against the Die.

Either the jets or the Die, or both, are kept in motion so that the jets of water cover the whole surface of the die. Multistage centrifugal or piston pumps are used; the important thing is to use water at the correct pressure. This should be about 350 lb. per sq. in. With lower pressures, the impact of the water is insufficient to clean the Die rapidly. Higher pressures do not achieve correspondingly quicker work, and are therefore not economical. Until recently, all Die Washing

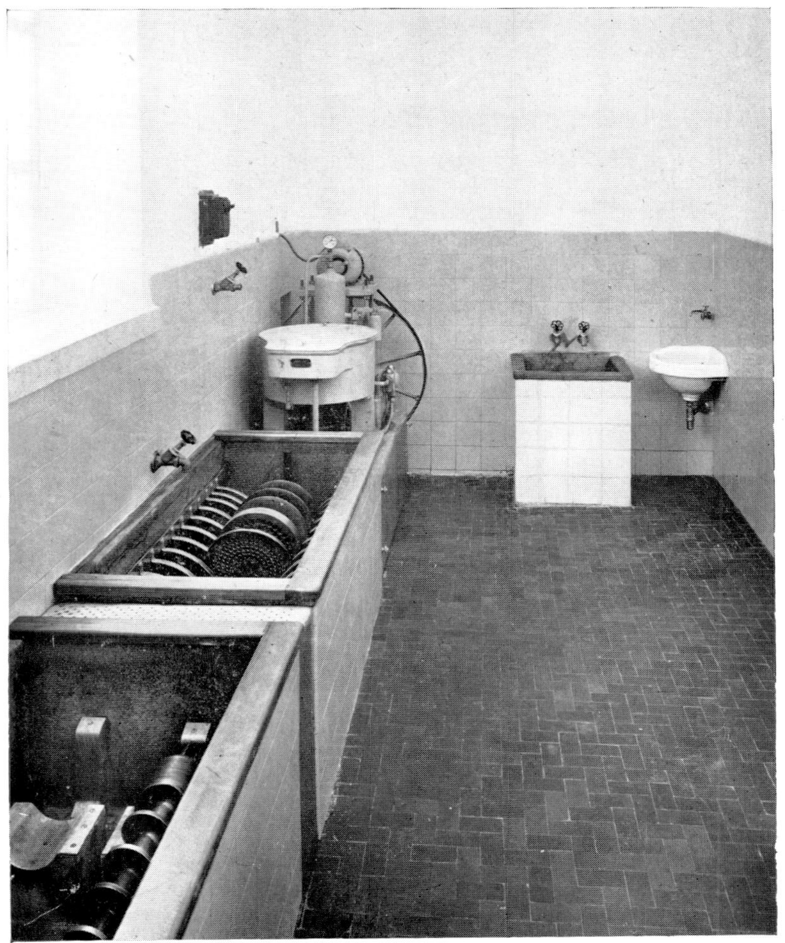

Fig. 51.—Die Room with soaking troughs and Die Washing Machine.

Machines were circular, as all the Dies handled were either round or square. With the advent of the Automatic Spreader using long Dies, special Die Washing Machines have had to be constructed. I illustrate on page 116 such a new Die Washing Machine which will handle both conventional round Dies and the long Dies used on a Spreader. Another illustration, Fig. 51, shows Die Room with soaking troughs for the Dies and Worm, and a Die Washing Machine for circular Dies.

Egg Dosers

All Macaroni Products are produced either as plain or egg products. When using the batch system the addition of the required amount of egg presented no problem. The desired quantity of egg was weighed on a scale, and tipped into the Batch Mixer with water and Semolina.

On the Continuous Extrusion Press this system does not work, and Continuous Egg Dosers have had to be designed. The first of these made by Buhler in 1938, consisted in the main of a receptacle of stainless steel into which the mixture of egg and water was introduced, and kept from settling by an Agitator. The receptacle is used in conjunction with a precision gear pump driven by a separate motor and speed regulator. By choosing the correct speed for the pump, any required amount of egg can be introduced into the Mixer of the Continuous Extrusion Press. If the Semolina used is fairly uniform in texture and humidity, the total amount of water can be mixed with the egg and pumped direct into the Mixer. With a Semolina of variable humidity and granulation, it may be advisable to mix only part of the water with the egg and to keep a small amount of water running into the Mixer. By regulating the amount of water that goes direct to the Mixer, it is possible to regulate the consistency of the dough without altering the speed of the pump, and without changing the proportion of egg to Semolina. The prescribed proportion must be adhered to within very close limits. If too little egg goes into the mixture difficulties are to be expected in meeting the requirements of any Regulations that may be in force, making it necessary to add not less than a certain amount of egg to products which are designated as Egg Macaroni Products, whilst too much egg means extra and unnecessary expense.

Therefore, it is essential to use a very accurate dosing pump, and an efficient mixing device which will maintain an even proportion of egg throughout the egg and water mixture. Egg being particularly liable to putrefaction, the Egg Doser must be kept meticulously clean. This point must be borne in mind when considering the design of this type of machine.

With the Buhler Continuous Egg Doser, the egg and water mixture is kept gently agitated by a pump continuously circulating part of the mix. The stainless steel vessel is quite smooth and easy to clean, and the pump may be washed with boiling soda water. The pipe feeding the egg and water mixture to the Continuous Extrusion Press also must be kept perfectly clean. Fixed pipes, even if made in stainless steel, are not satisfactory. The best arrangement is to use detachable rubber or plastic tubes, which can be cleaned very easily, and may be replaced at low cost when necessary. Also they are easily adjusted when an Egg Doser on wheels is used to feed several Continuous Extrusion Presses.

CHAPTER VII

DRYING MACARONI PRODUCTS

THERE is no doubt that drying is the most difficult operation in the manufacture of Macaroni Products. It is in fact one of the most delicate drying problems in the food industry, being more than simple dehydration as in the case of other alimentary products. In these simpler cases a certain amount of water has to be extracted from a food product, and the time required for the drying is only of economic importance; the drying temperature has seldom more than an upper limit, and the humidity of the drying air may be chosen by economic standards. This applies to fruit, vegetables, and meat, etc. In these cases the drying process and drying conditions can be worked out by a thermodynamic table and a slide rule, if drying in the sun is not considered satisfactory.

Unfortunately, the conditions are not so easy with Macaroni Products, as drying does not mean simply an extraction of a certain amount of water from the fresh goods. During drying Macaroni Products develop their final colour and texture. They must not warp or crack during the drying period, and must not crack after being packed and ready for sale. They must not be allowed to sour or show too much acidity, and they must develop the clear, appetizing taste of pure hard wheat, cook in a few minutes, and yet stand reasonably prolonged cooking without losing their shape and becoming pasty or watery.

As all these factors are to be taken care of, it is easy to understand why the drying problems of the Macaroni industry are more than just simple dehydration. Many Macaroni Product manufacturers consider paste goods drying to be an expert art, and the man in charge of the drying process is expected to have a wide experience and a certain intuition of what is good for Macaroni Products.

In the last few years a new drying technique has been evolved based on accurate scientific knowledge, which makes it possible to rule out the human element and to make perfect drying possible by any intelligent and conscientious operator.

Drying Macaroni Products in Batches

Until about the beginning of the twentieth century, it had been common practice to dry Macaroni Products either in the open or in large drying chambers. The first system was possible only in countries where the climate was suitable, and for this reason was mainly used in the southern part of Italy. Drying chambers could be worked in all countries, and this method has been used all over the world.

Large drying chambers are now obsolete, except for those still in use in some parts of Italy where they are used to dry long Macaroni Products, more especially Spaghetti. Travelling Fans are used in the large drying chambers, which may be considered to be the first step towards the modern Continuous Long Goods Driers. The large drying chambers were replaced by small drying chambers and Cabinet Driers. These can be considered to have been the standard type of Drier for the past forty years, but they are now gradually being replaced by large Continuous Driers. Cabinet Driers have been built by a number of firms, and many of these Driers differ only in minor details. I shall, therefore, describe only a few with certain characteristics, which are of particular interest.

The conventional drying process working in batches divides drying into three fundamental stages—pre-drying, softening period, also called sweating period, and final drying.

Pre-Drying Macaroni Products as they are Extruded

As the Macaroni Products leave the Die of a modern Continuous Extrusion Press, they are as a rule soft and warm and have a tendency to stick together, which makes it almost impossible to handle them without their being spoilt.

All Continuous Extrusion Presses, and practically all Hydraulic Presses, are therefore equipped with a fan blowing a current of air on to the Macaroni Products as they are extruded. According to the size and shape of the Macaroni Products, this current of air may be more or less powerful. Numerals and alphabets, for instance, should not be exposed to a strong air blast as they would be blown away, whilst Spaghetti and Macaroni may be subjected to almost any amount of air pressure from the moment they are extruded. Warm air, which means fairly dry air, is used normally where the surface is to be dried rapidly to facilitate further handling.

The first pre-drying is not only necessary to make the handling of the Macaroni Products possible, but it also helps to keep the Die and the cutting knife dry. Short cut goods extruded on a wet Die and cut with a wet knife, stick to the knife and to one another, making further handling tedious and uneconomical. Long Macaroni Products that have not been properly ventilated are awkward to handle, and spreading on sticks is extremely difficult; when the long hollow goods are cut in this condition the hole is often closed. This leads to trouble in the Driers, when it happens after the Macaroni has been cut free, and flat Macaroni, if it occurs when the Macaroni is still in connection with the Die.

In a normal Macaroni Die solid pins are used to provide the hole in the Macaroni. It has been suggested that where the diameter of the pin is sufficiently large, these pins should be made hollow. They could then be connected to atmospheric pressure, so that if any of the tubes of Macaroni become sealed, air would flow through them and thus prevent a collapse.

The air necessary for the first superficial drying operation is as a rule delivered by a Fan built into the frame of the Extrusion Press. In certain cases a pressure air system has been designed to provide a number of Presses with air from one central Fan. This system has been almost entirely abandoned, and modern Continuous Extrusion Presses are, with very few exceptions, equipped with built-in Fans which can be driven by the main motor, but an independent motor is generally provided for each Fan. A regulator is provided and a by-pass, which makes it possible to direct on to the Macaroni Products the quantity of air considered desirable. An air heater, generally operated by electricity, but which may be heated by steam or hot water, is sometimes built into the machine, thus making

Fig. 52.—Buhler Pre-Drier fitted with a number of oscillating sieves.

it possible to pre-heat the drying air if this is considered necessary.

Air distributors made of stainless steel, distribute this air regularly. Two different types of air distributors are used, one for short goods, and the other when making long Macaroni Products. These air distributors may be easily changed. The air distributor used when extruding short cut goods, is designed to blow air on to the Die and cutting knife. The air distributor for long goods, directs the air on to the long goods as they flow from the Die.

In the Buhler Continuous Extrusion Press the die holder carrying the Die is cast hollow, and is used as an air duct. Suitably placed apertures direct the air on to the Die, and on the Macaroni Products as they are extruded. These apertures are covered with a fine mesh screen to prevent small short cut products from being blown into the die holder. This construction has proved to be most efficient, as the major part of the air is directed on to the Die and the warm Macaroni Products as they are extruded, thus keeping the Die dry and providing a very good initial ventilation or pre-drying of the products. As well as being effective for both short cut and long goods, this construction obviates the necessity of removing the distributor each time the Die has to be changed.

Pre-Drying Short Cut Macaroni Products

Once the Macaroni Products have been cut from the Die they usually fall onto a pre-Drier. This is generally provided with an oscillating motion, and the short cut goods pass over a fairly fine mesh sieve. A Fan and an air heater situated below the sieve provide the necessary ventilation and heat.

Two different types of pre-Driers are now in general use. One uses a single oscillating sieve, while the other is provided with several sieves. The oscillating sieves are driven either by a balanced Oscillator or by an Eccentric Shaft. The balanced Oscillators require practically no maintenance, and run very smoothly. These are, therefore, to be preferred, particularly where vibration in the machine or in the building is objectionable. Generally speaking, these Oscillators are built in rather small sizes and therefore cannot be used where

Fig. 53.—Oscillating Spiral Pre-Drier made by Buhler.

heavy sieves must be operated; in such cases it is necessary to revert to the well-known Eccentric Shaft. The vibration set up by this drive can be compensated to a very large extent by using a number of sieves, and disposing them in two sets having a reciprocating motion generated by two eccentrics. In the illustration on page 123 the two sets of sieves are plainly visible, each being driven by a separate eccentric. Both eccentrics are mounted on the same shaft, and this arrangement proves most satisfactory. It makes possible a fair compensation of the oscillating force, and is therefore extensively used on all pre-Driers with a number of sieves. The balanced drive is more generally used on pre-Driers with a single oscillating sieve.

Some Continuous Extrusion Presses have the pre-Drier built underneath the Press itself; this is particularly the case with the Extrusion Presses built in Italy. Certain pre-Driers have an automatic feed for the trays, which is very desirable when short cut goods on trays are handled by women operators. The general arrangement is the same as on the Noodle Cutter.

The pre-Drier serves two distinct purposes—as a pre-Drier it is required to extract a certain amount of moisture from the short cut goods. Although the amount extracted is generally less than most people expect. On a machine with a single sieve, little more than $\frac{1}{2}$ per cent of moisture is evaporated. Pre-Driers with a number of sieves will extract up to 6–8 per cent, but this is exceptionally good. Pre-Driers generally provide only a superficial drying which might better be termed crusting, and gives to Macaroni Products a surface sufficiently hard to enable them to be handled without sticking or being crushed. The second and very important purpose of a pre-Drier, is to provide an inspection of the Macaroni Products as they leave the Extrusion Press. With the present-day automatic machinery it is essential that the short cut goods are open for inspection, before they enter the final continuous drying process. All pre-Driers should therefore have the top sieves open for easy inspection of the goods passing from the Press to the Driers.

The surface of the sieves over which the Macaroni Products are continually passing is subject to a considerable amount of wear and tear. They have to operate in an atmosphere that is warm and moist, and it is, therefore, essential that the mesh should be manufactured from stainless material. Tinned Wire is not suitable.

An original pre-Drier is illustrated on page 125. In this pre-Drier the sieve surface is not on the horizontal plane but has been constructed as a spiral, and the longitudinal oscillation of the sieve has been transformed into a circular oscillation. This construction gives a large drying surface on a reasonably small floor area. The short cut products are transported vertically during pre-drying, which can be of advantage in certain cases. The extraction of moisture on these pre-Driers is up to about 2 per cent, which is considerably higher than on an ordinary oscillating pre-Drier with one sieve.

Conveying Soft (Fresh) Short Cut Macaroni Products

From the Die, short cut goods should go to the pre-Drier in the shortest possible time, and with the absolute minimum of handling. Where possible they should fall straight from the Die on to the pre-Drier, and this should be situated as near as possible to the Die. Freshly made short cut goods are soft and delicate until they have been subjected to the first pre-drying operation. After they have passed the pre-Drier they may be handled without difficulty.

Horizontal conveying should be on trays and trolleys if manually operated, or on Belt Conveyors or oscillating conveyors if mechanical handling is practical or convenient. Vertical conveying of freshly made short cut goods is always a difficult problem. Pneumatic Conveyors are very efficient and easy to install and have had a certain amount of popularity, but they should not be used in modern plants except for the very small type of product such as rice, numerals, stars, etc.

The modern Continuous Extrusion Press produces a regular product of rich uniform colour, the appearance of which can be partially spoiled by pneumatic handling. Excluding exceptional cases, a pneumatic system always has two or more bends, and in these bends some of the short cut goods must of necessity be thrown against the walls of the conveyor tubes. The impact against the walls marks the goods, and these marks will be quite apparent in the finished product as clear patches, which spoil the otherwise good appearance of the short cut goods. Short cut goods extruded on an

Hydraulic Press do not show this loss of appearance to the same extent. Macaroni Products extruded on an Hydraulic Press are made from harder dough than the same goods extruded on a Continuous Extrusion Press. This harder dough produces goods lighter in colour and less regular. The small blurs or patches produced by pneumatic handling are therefore less conspicuous, but even in these cases, pneumatic handling of freshly made Macaroni Products cannot be recommended. Once the Macaroni Products are dried they may be handled on a Pneumatic Conveyor quite satisfactorily.

The handling of freshly made Macaroni Products must be reduced to an absolute minimum, and this can be achieved only by a proper layout of the Macaroni plant. Where vertical handling of fresh short cut goods cannot be avoided a normal Bucket Elevator is perhaps the best answer. The bottom of such an Elevator must be fitted with a drawer in order that the Elevator foot can be cleaned every day. Short cut goods that drop to the bottom of the Bucket Elevator, should never be left there for a sufficient length of time to allow them to get sour or to dry. The tube carrying the short cut goods into the Bucket Elevator should be narrower than the buckets, and arranged so that the goods are fed positively direct into the buckets. Short cut goods must not be allowed to fall into the bottom of the Elevator foot, nor to get behind the Elevator belt where they will be crushed between the belt and the pulley.

Pre-Drying Long Macaroni Products

As we have seen in a previous chapter (p. 49), long goods must be spread on sticks before they can be dried. These sticks are hung on wagonettes or trolleys, and wheeled into a cabinet. This cabinet is fitted with a Fan which circulates the air inside the cabinet. Air heaters may be built into the air circuit if it is considered desirable to heat the air, always a controversial point. Certain manufacturers claim that the best products are obtained without heating, others consider that heating of the air is advisable. I have seen absolutely first-class products produced both ways, and it depends rather on the drying room and how final drying is conducted, whether the pre-drying cabinet should be heated or not. The air as a rule is circulated once only through the pre-drying cabinets. Circulating the air in a closed circuit is quite exceptional, although this practice is the rule in the finishing Driers. The air should travel vertically to give the long goods a uniform

Fig. 54.—Spaghetti on sticks hanging on a wagonette being inserted into a Cabinet Drier for Long Goods.

I

pre-drying. Usually, the air is circulated from top to bottom, but it may also travel from bottom to top, or alternatively, both ways.

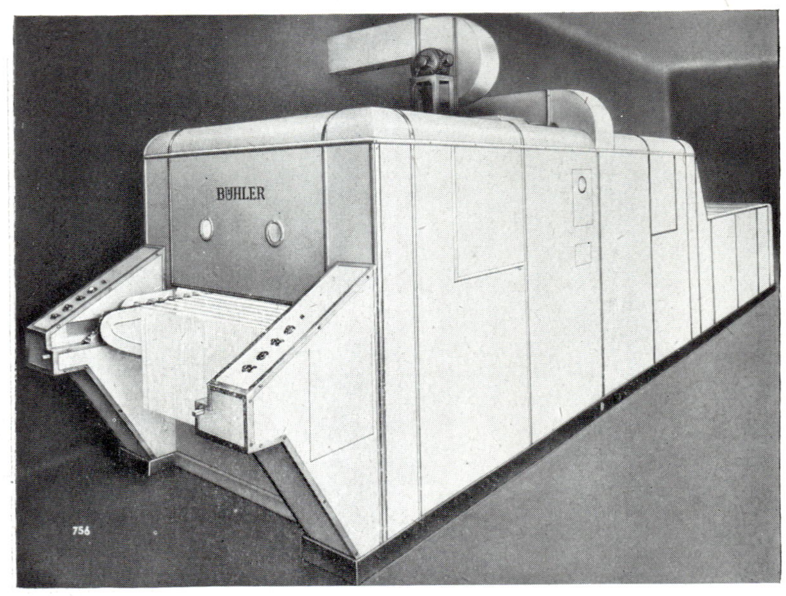

Fig. 55.—Buhler Pre-Drier for Long Goods.

Pre-drying must be as uniform as possible all around the long goods, and the best way to achieve this is by circulating the air from top to bottom. Alternating the direction of the air flow is not essential during pre-drying, and blowing the air from bottom to top results in too much agitation of the long goods. Blowing the air horizontally through the long goods will produce bent goods, and for this reason is not desirable. Alternating the direction of a horizontal air flow makes it possible to correct this difficulty to a certain extent, but it is not an ideal solution.

A remarkably good pre-Drier for Spaghetti has been developed by Buhler in connection with their Continuous Extrusion Press and the Spreader for long Macaroni Products. The sticks filled with Spaghetti are deposited automatically on a chain, and carried through a chamber about 15 ft. long, on a zigzag course that takes them through the total length of the

Fig. 56.—Cutting Macaroni to be dried in chassis.

chamber three times. Ventilation is arranged in such a manner as to provide not only very effective pre-drying, but also a sweating period. The sticks leave the pre-Drier at the far end on a chain at a convenient height to be taken off by hand, and are deposited on to wagonettes or trucks and wheeled into the finishing Drier.

Macaroni may also be handled on a chassis, a system developed by Yberty of Lyons. In this case as the Macaroni leaves the Die it is received on a sliding or oscillating table

Fig. 57.—Combined Drier showing left, trays for short-cut goods, and right, chassis for drying Macaroni and sticks for Spaghetti.

on which the chassis are fixed. The Macaroni fills the chassis, and is then cut to the required length by hand. To make this operation easier the side walls of the chassis have slots, the Macaroni being cut with a large knife, using the slots as a guide. The chassis are then arranged in the Drier, and the air blown through the holes of the Macaroni. If particularly straight Macaroni is to be produced it is redistributed by hand, and a piece of cardboard inserted between each row of horizontal Macaroni. This gives a perfectly straight and regular Macaroni which can be dried in twenty-four hours, but due to the fact that labour charges for this process are very high, it is rarely used to-day.

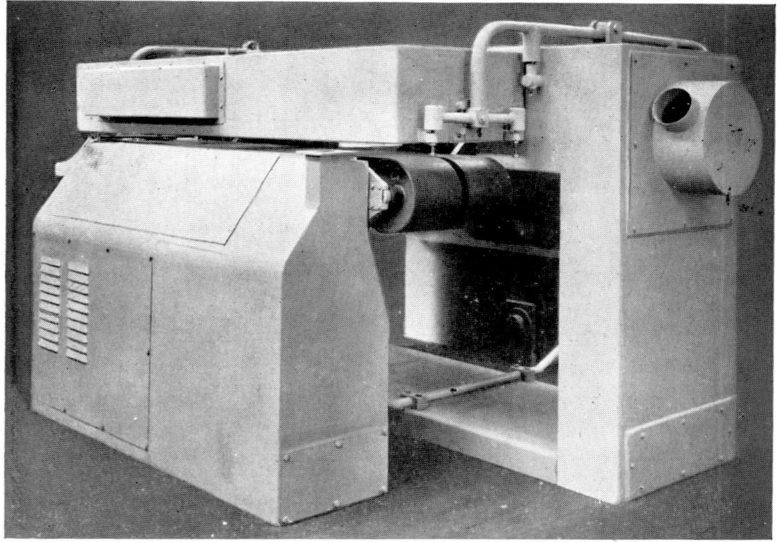

Fig. 58.—Automatic Cutting Device for Macaroni as installed in the factory of Mr. Dalang.

An automatic cutting device developed by Buhler in collaboration with Mr. Dalang, of Basle, Switzerland, makes this process more economical. When the Macaroni extruded through a long narrow die has attained the required length, a photo-electric cell starts a frame in motion which enables the Macaroni to be received on two belts. As soon as the belts have attained a horizontal position, a set of knives commences to cut the Macaroni to the required length. The trimmings produced go to a Trim Shredder and then back to the Press, whilst the Macaroni is carried by the belts to an Oscillating pre-Drier provided with different sections. The Macaroni is finally straightened by the Oscillating pre-Drier, and pre-dried to a sufficient extent to allow it to be put into chassis without getting bent and without sticking. The Oscillating pre-Drier may be followed by a larger machine of similar design in which the Macaroni is dried to the required moisture content, thus making the production of straight Macaroni by this method a continuous process.

Pre-Drying Noodles and Vermicelli

Scattered Noodles can be pre-dried on an Oscillating pre-Drier exactly like ordinary Elbows. Good pre-drying is particularly important for Noodles if they are to be loose and fluffy, which is a most desirable condition to facilitate final drying, and to make the finished products look so much better and appetizing. Exactly the same might be said of drying short cut Vermicelli.

Both Noodles and Vermicelli are often sold either twisted or folded, and in this case an Oscillating pre-Drier cannot be used. The curls are generally deposited on trays, and should be left on these trays until they have been dried to the required degree. Various preliminary Driers have been devised to handle these trays, the general idea being to blow a strong blast of air through the goods as they lie on the trays.

An Automatic Preliminary Drier for folds and curls has been placed on the market by Clermont. This Drier consists essentially of a large air chamber built to the length and width of the trays to be used. Large Fans induce a blast of air from the bottom of the chamber through the goods. The Clermont Corporation give the following description of how this Preliminary Noodle Drier works:

"The trays full of freshly folded Noodles are fed into the bottom of the air chamber. As soon as the entire tray has entered the chamber, an automatic mechanism raises it 6 in. into the chamber, leaving room for the passage of the next tray. When each new tray enters, all trays in the chamber are lifted 6 in., spacing the trays in process and leaving room for each new tray. The trays continue travelling upwards step by step until the first trays reach the top, then as each new tray enters the chamber, the topmost tray is automatically pushed out sidewise and caught by two arms which lower it step by step. The

Fig. 59.—Short Goods Drier using trays to be handled on wagonettes. This type of drier may be used for all short cut goods and curls.

lowered trays are automatically stacked on a flat-bottomed truck placed beneath this conveyor. As each truck is filled it is removed to the dry room, and replaced by an empty truck. The Noodles have received their preliminary drying process during their travel through the air chamber, and are now ready for the final process."

This Preliminary Drier is very efficient, and will extract about 25 per cent of the moisture that has to be removed.

Final Drying of Short Cut Macaroni Products

As they leave the pre-Drier the short cut Macaroni Products are received on trays and carried into the Drier for the final drying operation. The bottoms of the trays are made of stainless wire mesh, similar to that used on the

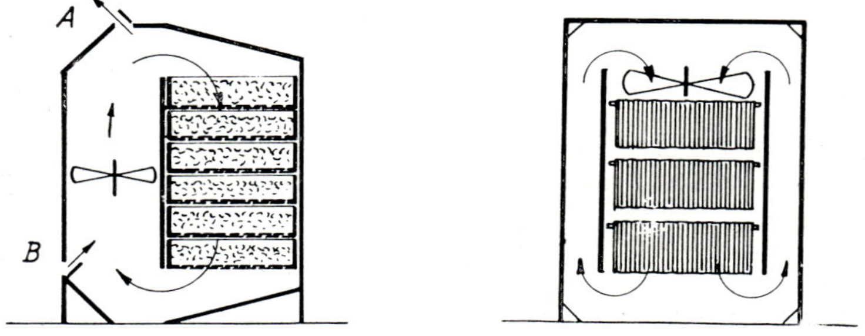

Fig. 60(a).—Diagram showing how the air is circulated vertically through the trays inside the Drying Cabinet.

oscillating sieve of the pre-Drier. The trays are piled into wagonettes, which are then wheeled into the Cabinet Drier—alternatively, the trays may be inserted directly into the Cabinet Driers without using wagonettes.

So far as drying is concerned, both systems are equivalent. Handling is made somewhat easier using wagonettes, on the other hand, the large number of wagonettes required makes the plant more expensive. If wagonettes are not used the trays are carried in stacks, and the whole stack pushed into the Cabinet Drier.

The main difference between the two systems lies in the air circulation. By using wagonettes in the Drier it is easy to turn all the trays by merely turning the wagonette. It is therefore possible to work with air always circulating in the one direction. With trays inserted directly into the Drier this method is not convenient, and therefore it is advisable to change the direction of the air circulation under these conditions.

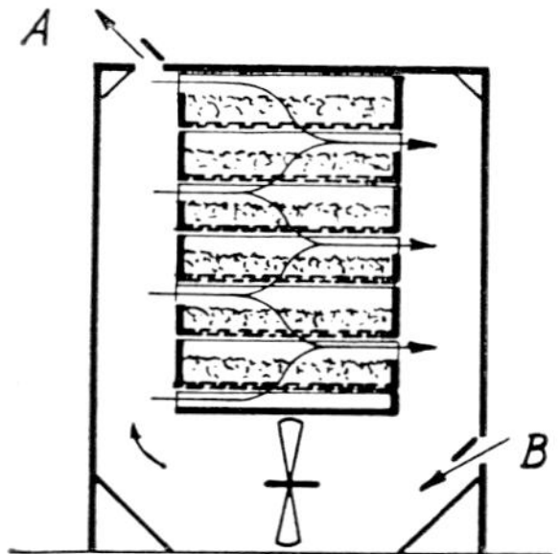
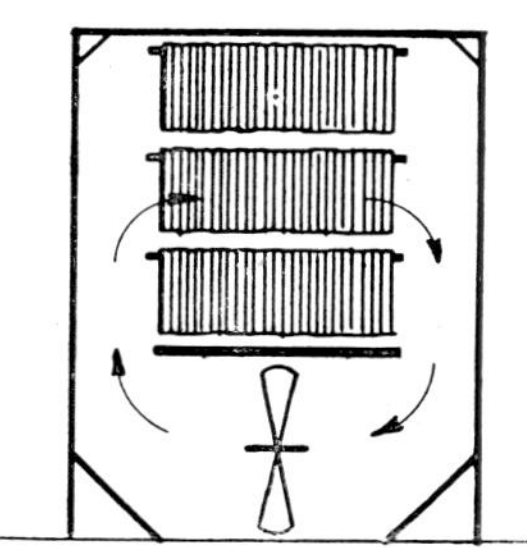

Fig. 60(*b*).—Diagram showing how the air is blown horizontally over the Macaroni Products.

Inside the drying cabinet the air may be circulated according to three different patterns. With the oldest method the trays form a vertical pile, and the drying air is circulated vertically through the whole pile flowing through all the trays in succession. It is necessary with this system to alternate the

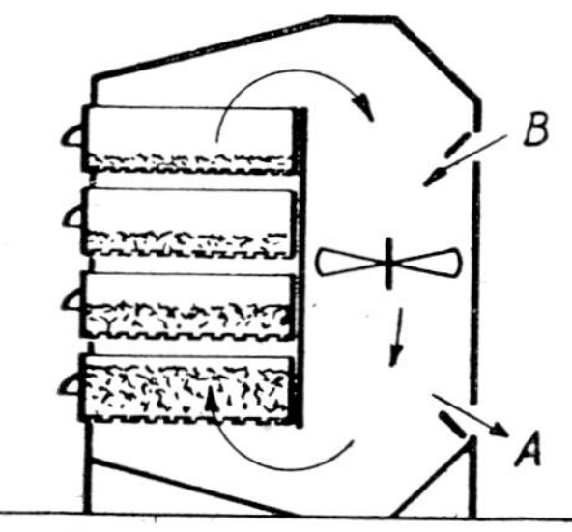
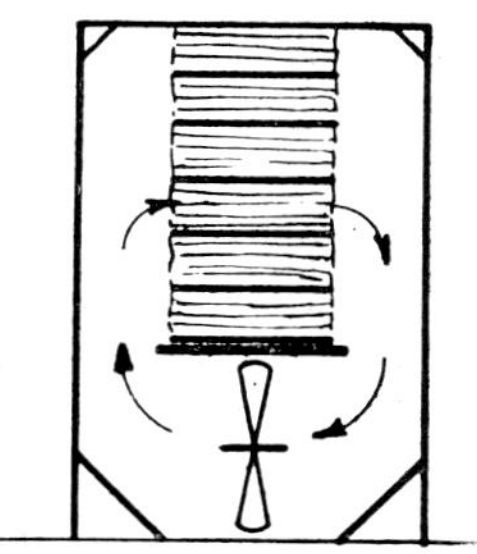

Fig. 60(*c*).—Diagram showing how the air is blown mainly horizontally through the Macaroni Products.

direction of the air flow, for instance, by changing the direction in which the Fan revolves. If this is not done, the goods on the top trays always receiving the fresh air, dry more quickly than the goods receiving air that has already flowed through the other trays, and which has become laden with moisture.

Fig. 60(b) shows the trays arranged for horizontal circulation of the drying air. This system has the advantage that all the trays are dried under the same conditions, but the fact that the air is not forced through the layers of Macaroni Products is a disadvantage. To compensate for this, the Macaroni Products should be disposed on the trays only in thin layers.

With the third system the horizontal trays are arranged in such a way that the air is forced to blow through the Macaroni Products. To achieve this the trays have one of their small sides higher than the other, and are so arranged as to have the high sides at alternative ends. As is immediately apparent from Fig. 60(c), the air is thus forced to pass through the Macaroni Product.

Cupboard Driers

After they have passed the pre-Drier, short cut Macaroni Products also may be delivered into cupboards, and the cupboards inserted into a Cabinet equipped with a powerful Fan. In this type of Drier, air is circulated vertically through the Macaroni Products. This Drier is very compact, but calls for considerably more work.

When the short cut goods come from the pre-Drier they are too soft to be filled into the cupboards to the full height. Therefore, it is customary to fill the lower half of the cupboards first, and when drying has proceeded for a certain time, to empty the contents of two cupboards into one, thus making space available for further Macaroni Products. Before drying is completed it is necessary to shuffle the goods in the cupboards once or twice to prevent sticking. This not only means extra labour, but as it is practically impossible to shuffle the goods without spilling some on the floor, there is always a certain loss. This type of Drier should therefore be used only with a very powerful pre-Drier, either a multiple pre-Drier, or two single pre-Driers in tandem.

Better results are obtained by using a modern Continuous pre-Drier, for instance, a Drum Drier, or the pre-Driers of the Buhler Continuous short cut Drier, which can be obtained as separate units.

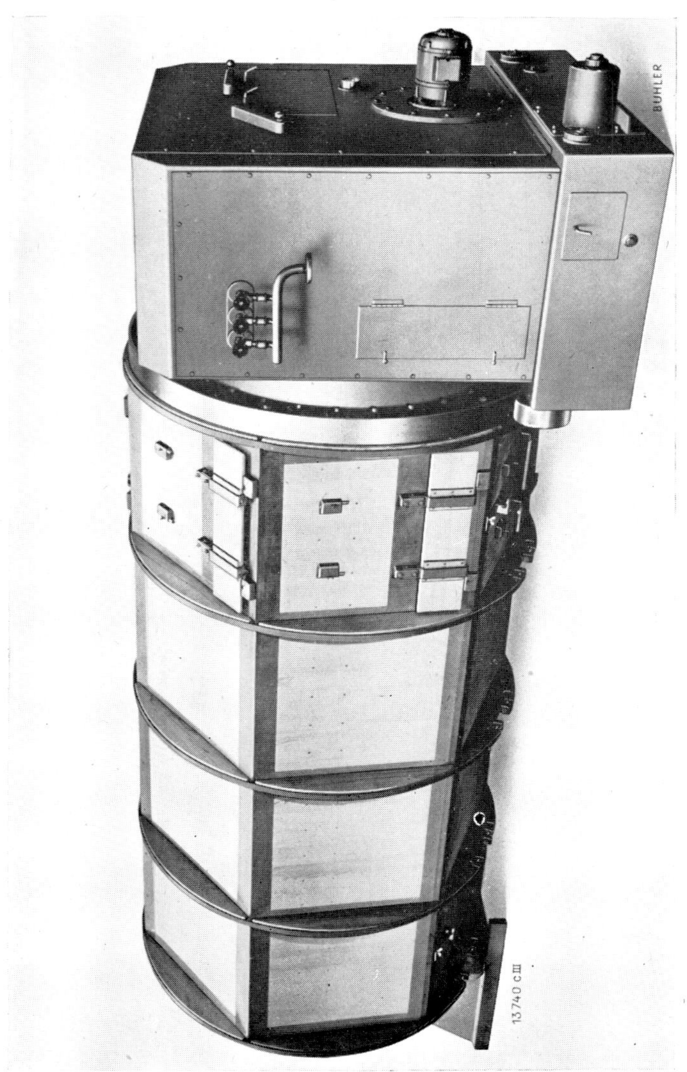

Fig. 61.—Buhler Drum Drier for Short Cut Macaroni Products.

Combined Driers

A combined Drier in which long and short cut Macaroni can be dried, may be seen on page 132. This Drier has three compartments. The one on the left is shown with a stack of trays for drying short cut goods. On the right-hand side, chassis are fitted to receive long Macaroni, and frames to receive Spaghetti on sticks. The central section is closed, showing the shutter regulating the air circulation. A Fan is built into the top of each section, which circulates the air horizontally through the Macaroni Products. The rotation of the Fan may be reversed, and thus the air may be circulated to and fro. This Drier can be recommended for small plants, unable to install special Driers for both long and short goods. By merely changing the interior equipment, any compartment of this Drier may be used for drying any type of Macaroni Product.

Large Batch Driers

A large Batch Drier of modern design for short cut Macaroni Products is illustrated on page 135. The short cut Macaroni Products are distributed on trays as they leave the Press, and the filled trays are placed on special wagonettes. These wagonettes, arranged in tandem, build up the Drier.

With this Drier particular care must be taken to ensure a regular flow of air over the whole surface of the trays, so that all the goods get almost exactly the same amount of ventilation. This will result in all the goods in a wagonette drying at the same time, a condition that is aimed at in all Driers, but attained by very few. The regular distribution of air is obtained by a system of air guides.

This Drier was one of the first endeavours to put drying on a scientific basis, utilizing a built-in thermostat to regulate the temperature, and a built-in hygrostat to regulate the humidity of the drying air. The thermostat acts on a motorized valve governing the steam going to the Air Heater, while the hygrostat regulates the humidity by opening and closing the valve admitting fresh air into the Drier. The exhaust valve is coupled to the valve admitting the fresh air, so that they always open and close accordingly. With this type of Drier it has been found possible to dry Macaroni Products according to a predetermined cycle, reasonably independent of atmospheric conditions. This plan, established according to the prevailing ideas on how Macaroni Products should be dried, runs on the following lines.

At first the Macaroni Products are dried in a warm, moist atmosphere, with heating on and the fresh air inlet valve partly closed. After a certain time the heat is reduced and the air valve completely shut—this is the sweating period. During this period humidity which is in the core of the Macaroni Product is travelling to the surface, and the surface which had started to develop a crust in the pre-drying period begins to get soft. After this sweating period a second drying period starts, during which drying proceeds with air a little cooler and drier than in the first period. As drying proceeds the air is set cooler and drier, until drying is practically completed. The air valves are now completely opened, and the Macaroni Products exposed to a draught of ambient air. The cycle is generally completed in about twenty-four hours. Using a little more heat at the beginning makes it possible to cut down the time required, whereas if only little heat is used drying time may go up to thirty-six hours. Drying too quickly is not an advantage to the quality of the Macaroni Products, as the flavour is not fully developed and resistance to excessive cooking is reduced. On the other hand if drying proceeds too slowly, especially at the beginning, too much acidity will develop and the goods will easily turn sour.

Generally, drying would be facilitated considerably if the short cut Macaroni Products could be gently agitated during drying. This would prevent the goods from sticking together, and, as the position of each particle of short cut goods would be continuously changed, each piece would get the same chance of losing its excess moisture regularly.

Drum Driers

The first answer to the problem of agitation was the Drum Drier. The first Drum Driers were built during the last century in France, and were known as Glaceurs. The Glaceurs are revolving drums, in which the Macaroni Products are exposed to a very warm, moist air and intense agitation. Drying proceeds very quickly, and can be reduced down to three hours. The goods coming from these Driers have a very poor colour, they show a characteristic polish, which as a rule is not desired, and although they are free from cracked or broken goods, they do not cook well. These goods are not considered to be of first-class quality, and, therefore, the Glaceurs have been practically abandoned, although they are perhaps to this day the most economic type of Drier.

In an endeavour to combine the advantages of the Cabinet and Drum Driers, a new type of Drum Drier has recently been developed by various firms. This drum is much larger in diameter than the old Glaceur, and works with average temperatures. It has a drying time of from 16 to 24 hours. The goods coming from these Drum Driers have very good cooking qualities, the flavour is good and acidity low, but they still have some of the undesirable polish, and the colour is not as rich as that which can be obtained in Cabinet Driers. A general view of such a Drum Drier with a capacity of about 18 cwt. of average sized Elbows is illustrated on page 139.

Capacity and output of a Drier, it must be remembered, are two very different things. The capacity of the Drier is measured by the quantity of Macaroni Products that the Drier will hold, and this capacity varies with the type of Macaroni Products being produced. Small soup pastes, rice and similar products have a heavy weight per cubic foot, and, therefore, the capacity of a Drier for such goods will always be large. Elbows, according to their size and the thickness of the walls, have a lighter weight per cubic foot, and for these products the capacity of the Drier is less. Scattered Noodles have the smallest weight per cubic foot, and consequently the capacity of the Drier is very low. The output of a Drier is the quantity of Macaroni Products that it will dry within a given period, i.e. 24 hours.

The total volume of the Drum Drier is sub-divided into small compartments, and during rotation the goods flow from one compartment into another. By this system the bulk of the short cut Macaroni Products is divided into small heaps; the heaps being small the goods are not so easily crushed, even when a soft dough is used, and polishing is reduced. General texture and colour are very superior to that obtained on a Glaceur.

By using a butterfly valve, as in the Buhler Drum Drier, the air can be easily guided so as to flow from the feed end to the tail end in one quadrant, and back in the opposite direction through the opposed quadrant, leaving the other two quadrants with practically no air flow. This means that as the drum rotates the goods first get the air blast from one side, they are then carried in a region of calm air and as rotation proceeds, the air blast comes from the other end to be succeeded by the second period of calm air. This cycle is repeated with every rotation of the drum, resulting in numerous and quickly alternating periods of drying and sweating. These alternating periods make very efficient drying possible, but care must be taken, if the best possible colour is to be obtained, not to use a drying air that is too dry. This is a defect frequently found in factories using this type of Drier, and results in goods of poor colour, and, in extreme cases broken products. Correction is simple, by enclosing the Drier in a small room in which the moisture in the air is maintained above 75 per cent relative humidity. This may be done by spraying water or by admitting a certain proportion of the exhaust air from the Drier into the room. It is convenient to have a hygrostat to regulate automatically the water spray or the exhaust valve.

Inside the drum the Macaroni Products are conveyed either by inclined baffles or by gravity. In the latter case, the drum is inclined, during the filling period, and is subsequently discharged at one end. This is the case with the construction illustrated on page 139, where the discharge doors can be clearly seen. When the Drier cannot be inclined, adequate doors, distributed over the whole length, are provided to discharge the finished goods.

Drum Driers are most popular in Italy where they are built by various firms.

Quite recently a new Drier has been put on the market by Buhler, which combines the advantages of the old Drum Drier with those of the old Cabinet Drier. The idea of this Drier has been to divide the Macaroni Products into very small heaps that are gently shuffled at longer intervals than is the case with Drum Driers, and to expose them to a succession of air and calm. With this Drier the goods being deposited in very small heaps, the dough may be made sufficiently moist and the sweating of the goods sufficiently intense, to produce

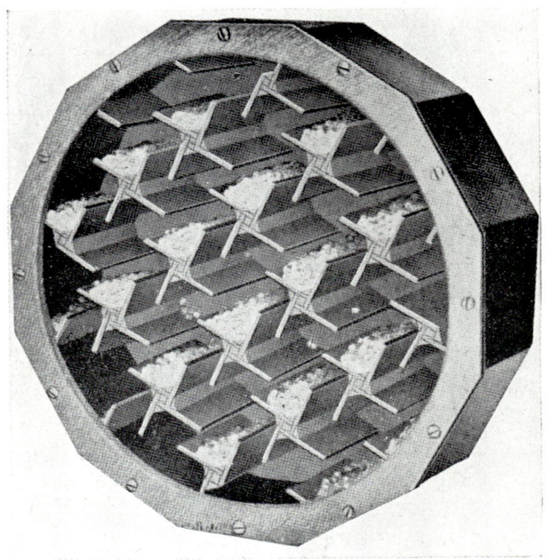

Fig. 62.—Section of Braibanti Drum Drier.

a very good colour without fear that the goods will stick or be crushed. Agitation being very gentle, the goods are not polished and little or no dust is produced. Dust with most types of Drum Driers is inevitable, and is most objectionable as it makes a Drier difficult to keep clean and free from insects. This new Drier works along the following lines.

The Macaroni Products coming from the Extrusion Press should pass over an ordinary pre-Drier to make control of the goods easier. They are then delivered into the feed inlet of the Drier, and flow into a channel made of woven wire carried on a frame. A type of worm conveyor is built inside the channel, which divides it into a number of small pockets. The channels are linked to a chain which runs over a large sprocket wheel, and so form a completely continuous sequence. As the sprocket wheel revolves, the channels are carried to the top of the Drier, and the Macaroni Products contained in each compartment roll gently over into the next compartment as the channel is carried over the top sprocket wheel. This is repeated in every channel, as each one passes over the sprocket wheel. Inside each channel the short cut Macaroni Products travel in small heaps, which all advance one pocket at a time at each revolution.

In about two hours the product has travelled the whole length of the Drier. They are now delivered either to a rotating tube, which carries them back to the inlet to repeat their journey through the Drier, or they leave the machine by the outlet. These Driers may be worked as single units, in which case the products are carried repeatedly through the Drier until they are completely dried, or may be arranged as a battery, in which case each Drier delivers into the next the Macaroni Product that has passed through the unit. This combination makes continuous drying possible.

Fig. 63.—Buhler Short Goods Drier, Type CGpc.

Two Fans keep the air circulating through each Drier, the air first being forced through an Air Heater, and then through the channels and the Macaroni Products situated at the bottom of the Drier. The air then travels between the vertical sets of channels and the outer part of the Drier to the top, passes through the channels and the Macaroni Products at the top, where it is picked up again by the Fan, and repeats the cycle. A small opening which may be regulated admits the necessary fresh air, and an Exhaust Fan. takes the air carrying the moisture out of the Drier.

This Drier has an output of 10–40 cwt. per day, depending upon the weight per cubic foot and the type of products to be dried. Drying times vary from 6 to 13 hours according to the product to be handled. For plants that are not large enough to justify a Continuous Drier, this type of Drier is most suitable. It will handle all types of short cut Macaroni Products, times and temperatures being regulated to suit each individual requirement. The goods are not polished, and labour is reduced to a minimum.

These Driers may be equipped with thermostatic control of the heat using a motorized valve governed by a thermostat, and hygrostatic control of the moisture of the drying air, by a motorized valve for the fresh air, synchronized with the exhaust valve governed by the hygrostat.

Short Cut Macaroni Product Driers Incorporated in the Building

All the short cut Driers described in the previous pages are Cabinet Driers mainly built from wood or similar material. Some of these Driers have also been built with bricks. This construction has been particularly popular in Italy, and with manufacturers of Italian descent.

The standard Cabinet Driers are light, and if necessary may be moved easily as the output of a plant increases, or if changes are to be made in the plant layout. Driers built into the building cannot be moved without being destroyed at least in part, but they have the advantage of being cheap. Lime-washed once a year they keep clean and can be insulated easily, thus they use the heat required for drying with high efficiency and at the same time show very little condensation.

Final Drying of Long Macaroni Products

Long Macaroni Products, as we have seen earlier in this chapter, are mostly dried on sticks, a much smaller proportion being dried in chassis, with or without using cardboard between each layer of goods.

Many different types of Driers for long Macaroni Products have been constructed to handle sticks for the final drying after the pre-drying operation. Most of these are fairly large cabinets holding from 6 to 40 cwt. of goods distributed in two or three layers. The sticks carrying the long goods are either handled on wagonettes or racks, the general arrangement being practically the same as for the pre-Drier. Ventilation on the most recent Driers is vertical, in other words, parallel with the goods to be dried. Driers for long Macaroni Products using a horizontal air blast are found only infrequently, as such Driers are liable to the same difficulties as the corresponding pre-Drier (p. 30), and for the same reason produce bent goods.

The various constructions of long goods Driers differ mainly in the manner of guiding and circulating the air used for drying. A very popular Italian construction used by Garbuio has four propellers, with, as a rule, four blades to each, fixed to a common vertical shaft driven by an electric motor. The propellers force the air to flow through the goods vertically from top to bottom. The two opposite sides of the Drier not used for doors are double-walled, thus forming a passage to bring air back from the bottom to the top. A valve in connection with the Fan at the floor level provides an exhaust for the moist air, and a corresponding amount of fresh air is admitted by a second valve in connection with the small Fan at the top end of the shaft.

Where the exhaust air is to be delivered outside the drying room, the exhaust valve must be connected to a duct, and in such cases the exhaust valve is often found at the top of the Drier for convenience. Carrying the moist air outside the building is to be recommended in all cases, as the exhaust air from the Driers makes the atmosphere in a drying room uncomfortable, and particularly during cold weather may give rise to very considerable condensation on the walls and ceiling.

One of the details that requires most careful consideration

Fig. 64.—Buhler Long Goods Drier, Type CGpl.

is the regularity of the air flow through the Drier. Almost all long goods Driers have a fairly large section, and this is one of the reasons why it is so difficult to get a satisfactory uniform flow of the drying air. Nearly always there are parts of the Drier where the air speed is low and drying is slow, which necessitates the whole batch being left in the Drier until the goods in the slow part have caught up with the rest. This irregular drying delays the process, and accounts for the drying time of up to three days required for long goods. Driers having a small cross-section in which the air flow is fairly regular, have shorter drying times. This is the case with the Drier illustrated on page 132, in which Macaroni and Spaghetti are dried in 24 hours. Larger Driers in which the air flow is properly controlled, dry Spaghetti in 30 to 36 hours.

In the same way as we have seen with the drying of short goods, long Macaroni Products are handled better and more quickly using motorized valves governed by hygrostats and thermostats, so maintaining inside the Driers the air condition considered most suitable.

A remarkable Drier for all long Macaroni Products is an intermediate construction between the standard Cabinet Drier and the modern Continuous Drier. The Macaroni Product to be dried is handled in batches and once the Drier has been filled the goods do not stay in one position, but continue to travel steadily through the Drier during the whole drying process. Thus, the Macaroni Products are carried through all the possible positions inside the Drier in regular succession, and automatically get the same drying quite independent of any irregularity in the air flow. Perfect drying is thus achieved in from 15 to 36 hours according to the product being handled.

The Macaroni Products are spread on sticks either by hand or by a mechanical Spreader. The correct number of sticks are then deposited on a frame or rack, and the frame pushed on to a rail fixed at a convenient height inside the Drier. The frame, complete with sticks and Macaroni Product, now occupies the position immediately inside the Drier, and by a semi-automatic mechanism the frame is carried upwards. When a second frame is introduced the first frame goes to the top of the Drier, and the second frame then travels upwards. As the first frame reaches the top of the Drier it begins to travel along horizontally, and as further frames are introduced they join the first frame at the top and so gradually completely fill the top portion of the Drier.

When the first frame arrives at the far end of the Drier it is carried downwards to rails situated immediately under the top set of frames, from which the long goods are suspended. This process continues until the Drier has been completely filled from top to bottom, with four separate layers of frames filled with sticks, from which the Macaroni Products are hanging. The mechanical system built into the Drier now keeps the frames circulating continuously in a closed circuit, one complete circuit taking about $2\frac{1}{2}$ hours. Once the long goods have been dried they can be taken out of the Drier by simply reversing the operation of the charging period, the speed of discharge being regulated according to the personnel available to handle the dried goods.

A Fan keeps the air inside the Drier circulating in a closed circuit. A built-in Air Heater for use with steam, hot water or electricity, provides the required heat, and valves provide the necessary fresh air and exhaust the moist air. Temperatures and humidity of the air inside the Drier may be controlled by using motorized valves in connection with thermostats and hygrostats.

By considering the flow of the Macaroni Products and the flow of the air, it will be seen that the Macaroni Products first go into a zone where there is practically no ventilation. They next enter a zone where they are exposed to the warm air coming from the Air Heater. After this they enter a zone of relative calm, where the moisture inside the Macaroni Products gets a chance of travelling to the surface, thus preventing crusting.

In the next zone the Macaroni Products are ventilated by the air which is now cooler and moist, having travelled through all the Macaroni Products, and sweating which started in the previous section is intensified. After this follows another zone with practically no ventilation, and then the whole cycle is repeated. As drying proceeds temperatures and humidity of the air are regulated according to the size of the Macaroni Product in the Drier. If the Driers are located in an air-conditioned room it will be an easy matter to set the temperature and humidity cycle, thus making this type of Drier practically automatic.

Prolonged tests have proved that all types of long Macaroni Products can be dried in this type of Drier with exceptionally good results.

Long goods Driers incorporated in the building have been used to an even larger extent than built-in Driers for short goods. The interior of a long goods Drier is very simple, especially when wagonettes and racks are used to carry the sticks, and the use of such built-in drying cabinets has become very popular for long goods. The advantages and drawbacks are essentially similar as for short goods Driers built on similar lines.

CONTINUOUS DRIERS FOR SHORT CUT MACARONI PRODUCTS

Once the Continuous Extrusion Press had shown that it was possible to abandon the old batch system and to produce Macaroni Products as a continuous process, the demand for Continuous Driers came quite naturally. In the same way continuous Weighing and Packing Machines will be asked for, as soon as continuous drying is in more general use.

Some of the batch Driers, which I described earlier, may be used to build up a continuous drying system. This has already been done with short goods by using a number of Drum Driers arranged as a battery. By utilizing an Oscillating Conveyor, which has proved to be a most suitable feeding system, the fresh goods coming from the pre-Drier are carried to the first Drum Drier. When this first Drier is filled, the goods are conveyed to the second Drier, and so on until all the Driers are filled. When the drying process has been completed the goods are discharged on to a Belt Conveyor or another Oscillating Conveyor, and carried to bins or direct to the weighing and packing machinery. Such a plant makes continuous production possible, although, strictly speaking, this type of drying is not continuous, but rather a mechanized batch system.

A fully continuous drying system can be built up where a number of Buhler Drum Driers are arranged so that the first Drier feeds into the second, the second into the third and so on, the number of units depending on the output required. As this type of Drier discharges at the top and the inlet is at the bottom, it is possible to feed from one Drier into the next without using any intermediate Conveyor. The drying conditions are set in each Drier according to the advance of the drying operation, for instance, the first unit may be run as a very efficient pre-Drier, the second as a sweating unit, and the third and fourth as finishing Driers. The goods are dried as they travel through the Driers, conditions in each Drying unit being kept constant. This is characteristic of the Continuous Drier, whereas, with the batch Drier the goods stay in the same unit during the whole of the drying process, the conditions inside the Drier being changed as the drying proceeds.

Hoskins Continuous Drier

This was one of the first units built to dry short goods as a continuous process. The manufacturers give the following description of this very successful Drier:

"The Hoskins Continuous Short Goods Drier consists of four drying units, namely, a Preliminary Drier and three finishing Driers. These units are connected in series by means of Belt Conveyors.

"In the latest model, the Prelimary Drier consists of a sheet metal cabinet, approximately 24 ft. long × 9 ft. high × 5 ft. wide, containing four continuous conveying screens, with an air conditioning unit attached to the side of the cabinet.

"Wet Macaroni enters the top of the Drier through a Drum Spreader, which distributes it across the 5 ft. width of the top screen. The Spreader consists of a rotating cylinder open at one end, and sloped at an angle of 5° from the horizontal. The cylinder is divided into eight compartments by radial metal sheets running the length of the cylinder. Each of the compartments discharges through a hole in the shell of the cylinder at a different point across the width of the drying screen. As the drum revolves, Macaroni fed into the open end of the Spreader works its way down each of the compartments to the discharge openings.

"Air is circulated through the screens in the Drier by means of two centrifugal blowers in the air conditioning unit. The dry bulb temperature of the air is automatically controlled by a thermostat, which regulates the steam supply to a finned tube coil in the air conditioning unit. The wet bulb temperature is controlled by means of a wet bulb thermostat and dampers, which regulate the amount of humid air exhausted from the Drier. Approximately half of the moisture to be removed from the Macaroni is taken out in the Preliminary Drier in about 30 minutes. The remaining moisture is removed over a period of 12 hours in the three finishing Driers."

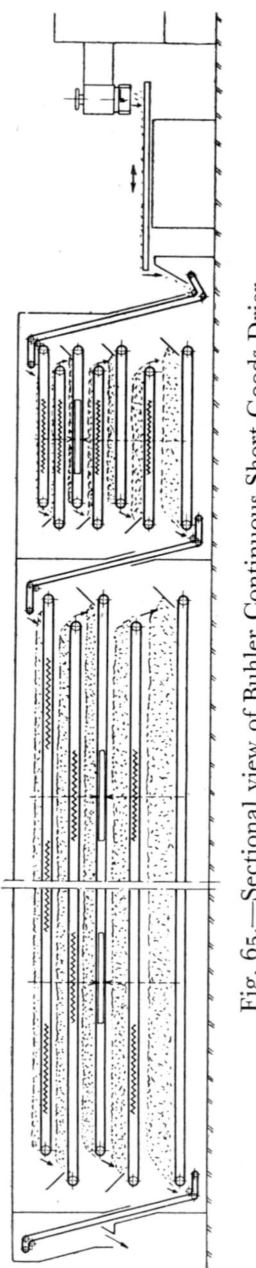

Fig. 65.—Sectional view of Buhler Continuous Short Goods Drier.

The finishing Driers are identical with the Preliminary Drier, with the exception that a resting or "sweating" screen is added over the top of the drying screens on each Drier. This screen is separated from the air circulation by means of a sheet metal partition.

Buhler Continuous Drier

A cross-section is shown in the diagram on page 153 from which it will be seen that the Drier is constructed in two parts and built into a single unit. The first part acts as an exceptionally efficient pre-Drier, and the second finishes the drying and delivers the goods thoroughly cooled and ready for packing. On the first conveyor of the pre-Drier section the goods are handled in a very thin layer so that they shall not stick or become deformed. This conveyor travels at a relatively high speed, and after a few minutes the goods are discharged on to the second conveyor. This travels at a somewhat slower speed and consequently the layer of goods is now thicker, which, considering the ventilation the goods have received on the preceding conveyor, is possible without disadvantage.

From the second conveyor the goods drop on to the third and so on, each conveyor travelling a little slower than the preceding one, and the layer of goods getting a little thicker on each successive conveyor. This makes perfect drying possible, and at the same time allows for a compact and economical Drier. The conveyors are of an original and very efficient design, having a big advantage over the wire mesh type of conveyor where the many points of metallic contact cause friction, and consequently wear and tear takes place.

Each conveyor element of the Buhler Conveyor Belt has no contact with the other conveying elements, and each is carried by a shaft running in a bearing with permanent lubrication. The individual elements have a Z-like shape.

The Macaroni Products are carried by these conveying elements in heaps, the size of which increases as the Macaroni Products become drier. The elements do not fit closely but have a gap between each other, and it is the angle of friction which keeps the goods on the conveyor. Thus jamming or overflowing is permanently eliminated, and without mechanical difficulty. The air is carried through the Macaroni Products, thus ensuring regular and efficient drying. When the conveying elements reach the pulley they open completely, and allow the Macaroni Products to be discharged on to the next conveyor.

The Air Heaters are built in between the conveyors, part of the heat being transmitted to the air, and part of it directly into the goods by radiation. It is thus possible to give the

Fig. 66.—Barducci Drier for Long Macaroni Products.

Macaroni Products the exact amount of heat required for the best drying conditions, and at the same time this intermediate heating provides for the best possible thermal efficiency. On the last conveyors the heat is shut off, and the Macaroni Products get a strong ventilation which cools them through to the core and prepares them ready for packing.

Buhler have developed a new drying technique, to which I shall refer in a separate chapter devoted to the theoretical side of Macaroni drying. According to these new ideas perfect drying can be conducted without accurate temperature and humidity control. Of all the modern Driers, the Buhler Continuous Drier is the only one working practically without thermometer and hygrometer. They require no conditioned room, and can be installed in any adequately heated and ventilated premises. The fresh air is taken directly from the room, and the exhaust air being practically saturated must be taken outside the building by a special exhaust pipe. A booster Fan should be built into this pipe except where the pipe is very short. If the air in the premises in which the Driers are installed should be too dry, part of the exhaust from the Drier may be diverted into the room to attain the required humidity.

Drying time on the Buhler Continuous Short Cut Goods Drier can be set according to requirements. The perfectly regular distribution of the air, the gentle movement of the goods as they fall from one conveyor to the next, and the correct distribution of the heat, together make it possible to work with a very short drying time without producing cracked or broken goods. If the best possible results are to be obtained, including good flavour, colour and cooking qualities, the drying time should not be too short. Buhler recommend 12 to 16 hours, according to the shape and size to be dried and the quality of the Semolina.

CONTINUOUS DRIERS FOR LONG MACARONI PRODUCTS

Long goods are more difficult to handle and require longer time to dry than short goods. Up to the present time only one firm has marketed a unit for the continuous production of long goods from Semolina to the finished dried long Macaroni Products. The first step to such a production unit can be seen in the Barducci Drier for long goods, used mostly in the southern part of Italy. The sticks covered with long Macaroni Products are arranged in a long channel on two or three storeys. A fan running on a rail travels to and fro under the goods producing on its passage a strong current of air. Thus, the long Macaroni Products receive a strong ventilation as the fan passes, and fall back into a calm atmosphere when the fan has passed. Here again, we find the alternating drying and resting which I have referred to when discussing batch Driers. With this type of Drier charging and discharging requires manual labour.

A Continuous Long Goods Drier built on similar lines to the Short Goods Drier has been developed in Italy. Long goods, particularly Spaghetti, are distributed on sticks on a wagonette in the usual manner. The wagonettes are closed at one end and pushed into the channel, all the wagonettes having their closed end in the same direction. The channel is thus divided by the wagonettes into a number of compartments, each compartment holding a certain amount of Spaghetti. The sides of the channel are fitted with Fans, one Fan corresponding to each compartment. At regular intervals, depending on the capacity of the Drier and the amount of Spaghetti carried by a wagonette, a new wagonette is introduced into the drying channel by means of a mechanical device. At the same time a wagonette filled with dried Spaghetti leaves the channel at the far end. Some of these channel Driers have been preceded by a standard pre-Drier in which the Spaghetti has been thoroughly pre-dried. This arrangement requires extra space and labour, but makes further handling of the Spaghetti in the channel Drier easier, the first drying hours generally being decisive for the final result.

Good results have been obtained on this type of Drier, but they do require a great deal of manual labour. The Spaghetti has to be spread on the sticks, the sticks deposited individually on to the wagonettes, and the wagonettes handled in and out of the channel. As the wagonettes leave the Drier with the dried Spaghetti, it must be taken off the sticks by hand. The filling and discharging of the wagonettes also requires a fair amount of floor space.

Drying in this type of Continuous Drier is practically the same as in a standard batch Drier. In each compartment the drying air is kept at a temperature, humidity and speed corresponding to the condition of the Spaghetti inside the particular compartment. In the standard batch Drier the Spaghetti remains in the same position for the whole of the drying time, and the conditions inside the cabinet are changed as drying proceeds. In the channel Drier the Spaghetti travels from one compartment to the next, and as each compartment has its own permanent drying condition, the effect is exactly the same as in a conventional batch Drier. The drying schedule is established by the man in charge of the drying, and the Spaghetti dries the same way during the whole process. The individual compartments are small, and as the Spaghetti travels from one compartment to the next, each piece of

Spaghetti gets practically the same treatment and drying proceeds very regularly. This type of Drier has been used in Italy for drying Spaghetti, and for this product drying time has been reduced to about 24 hours.

Buhler Production Unit for Long Macaroni Products

In 1946 Buhler Bros. erected the first Continuous Production Unit for producing long Macaroni Products in a continuous operation. From the bins in which the Semolina is stored to the finished long Macaroni Products ready for packing, no handling is required. A conveying system carries the Semolina to the feeding belts of the Buhler Extrusion Press. This is fitted with a special spreader arm to distribute the long Macaroni Products on to the sticks, which are then handled by a mechanical Spreader built into the head of the Continuous Long Goods Drier. The sticks loaded with long Macaroni Products are carried over a cutter, which cuts the long goods to the exact length required. The trimmings fall on to a Belt Conveyor, where they are carried to a Shredder and immediately returned to the Mixer of the Press. By this means not an ounce of dough is lost.

The sticks filled with long Macaroni Products are then carried by the chain of the Spreader to the top of the Drier, and start travelling down. On this downward movement the sticks are lifted out of the carrier by three pendulums and deposited on to the drying chains. The first stick goes to the first drying chain, the second stick to the second chain, the third stick to the third chain, and then the fourth stick to the first chain, the fifth to the second, and so on. In this manner sticks that are in the same vertical plane on the three chains are filled on the Spreader in succession, they are, therefore, all practically of the same age and in exactly the same condition. The drying chains carry the sticks through a number of compartments, the exact number of these compartments depending upon the output of the Drier.

Each compartment contains a Fan, circulating the drying air in the usual manner from top to bottom. Valves are provided for the intake of fresh air, and the exhaust of the air fully charged with humidity. In the first few compartments Air Heaters are provided above each row of sticks. The

Fig. 67.—Buhler Continuous Production Unit for Long Macaroni Products.

Heaters are set in such a manner as to produce air of equal drying power for each row of sticks. It is then possible to dry all the long goods according to exactly the same schedule, and to produce Macaroni Products dried to a very strict specification.

When a little over half the moisture to be taken out has been evaporated, only one heater for all three rows of sticks is required. Only very little moisture is now absorbed by the air, and therefore the temperature and moisture content of the air does not vary sufficiently from the first row to the third to produce substantial changes in the drying. In the last compartment heat is completely shut off, the inlet and outlet valves are opened, and the long goods are cooled and conditioned to the outside atmosphere, thus making them ready for packing.

At the end of the Drier the sticks are lifted by a second set of pendulums and deposited into the carriers of the stripping device, which mechanically strips the long goods from the sticks and deposits them on a table ready for packing.

For their Continuous Production Unit, which handles both solid and hollow goods with equal efficiency, Buhler utilize an exceptionally long stick, nearly 7 ft. in length, made from stainless steel, which has proved to be most successful. On any standard Drier such a long stick would be most awkward to handle, but on the Continuous Production Unit, the sticks being handled mechanically, the use of a long stick is not a disadvantage. By utilizing these long sticks it has been found possible to construct a compact Drier with a high rate of production.

Drying time on the Buhler Unit is as a rule 24 hours for all types of long goods, but if necessary this time may be reduced to about 18 hours. All types of long goods can be handled in the same length of time, as with this type of Drier Buhler have developed a new drying technique which does not use the classical periods of pre-drying, sweating and final drying, but which dries according to a continuous predetermined schedule. This schedule does not work to the standard idea based on temperature and humidity of the drying air. The Buhler Unit can work without thermometer and hygrometer. Details of the thermodynamic working of this Unit are dealt with in a separate chapter devoted to the theory of drying.

The regularity of the moisture content of the long goods dried in this Unit is very remarkable. By choosing the correct setting almost any required moisture content can be maintained to within 0·2 per cent. This is of considerable economic importance. If a moisture content of 12 per cent is prescribed and Macaroni Products of very good keeping qualities are required, a batch Drier drying with a regularity of plus and minus 1 per cent must be set to dry down to 11 per cent so that the long goods having the higher moisture content should not have more than the prescribed 12 per cent. The average moisture content will be nearer 11 per cent. The Buhler Unit can be set to produce 11·8 per cent, so that the long goods with the higher moisture content will not have more than 12 per cent and the driest not less than 11·6 per cent. This means that the Buhler Unit will yield almost 1 per cent more marketable Macaroni Products from the same quantity of Semolina.

When Macaroni Products of widely different weights per unit have to be handled on the same production unit, it may be advantageous to run the Drier with adjustable speeds and to take advantage of the possibility of drying light Spaghetti in a shorter time than heavier Macaroni.

When drying light Spaghetti, the quantity of Macaroni Product that can be accommodated on a stick is considerably less than the quantity of heavy Macaroni that may be placed on the same stick. If the number of sticks going through the Drier in a given time is the same in both cases, the output of Spaghetti will be considerably less than the output of Macaroni. By using a variable speed motor, the output can be stepped up by increasing the speed of the sticks through the Drier. A new limit is set, however, by the extrusion speed and the output of the Extrusion Press. The increased speed of the sticks means a corresponding reduction in the drying time, which in most cases will be found to be acceptable for light Macaroni Products.

Continuous Automatic Noodle Drier

A Continuous Automatic Noodle Drier has been built by the Consolidated Macaroni Corporation. This machine dries the Noodles on a number of conveyors made of woven wire.

K

On the Noodle Drier the clearance over the screens is particularly high in order to accommodate the Noodles which are light and bulky. As Noodles are among the Macaroni Products which dry most easily, these Continuous Noodle Driers can be set to dry in the comparatively short time of from 6 to 8 hours.

NEW DRYING SYSTEMS

Up to a few years ago only air and heat were considered for the drying of Macaroni Products. It was either direct solar heat in the old open drying rooms used in Mediterranean Countries, or the heat taken from the drying room in Cabinet Driers without incorporated Air Heaters. In modern Driers, part of the heat required and in most cases the total heat required for the drying process, is introduced by Air Heaters built into the Drier itself. The heating unit may be operated by electricity, hot water, or steam.

Infra Red

Recently, other means of drying Macaroni Products have been considered including the use of Infra Red. Properly handled, Infra Red will dry Macaroni Products most successfully, particularly short cut goods, yielding a perfect product. Unfortunately, up to now it has not been possible to achieve really economical drying with Infra Red. When drying Macaroni Products Infra Red lamps act mainly as a source of heat. To obtain a good distribution of heat over all the Macaroni Products when commercial quantities are to be handled, it is necessary to use a large number of lamps. The distance between the lamps and the Macaroni Products should be not less than 10 in., which makes it necessary to have the different layers of Macaroni Products about 30 in. apart. Thus a Drier using Infra Red will be larger, and, therefore, more expensive than a corresponding Drier of conventional design.

It has been suggested that with Infra Red the drying time can be reduced considerably, but this is not the case. We have seen that with the French Glaceur, Elbows can be dried in three hours, but their quality is not good. Short drying times down to an hour and even less have been obtained using heat generated by electricity or steam, but all these short, quick drying processes have not up to now given a first-class product. If drying time is increased to give a perfect Macaroni Product, the Infra Red Drier will be more expensive to build and to run than a properly built Drier of conventional design. It has also been suggested that Infra Red will penetrate to the core of the Macaroni Products and dry them from the interior. Tests have shown this to be an illusion. Infra Red is certainly the best means of drying a thin film of varnish on an automobile body, and is most effectively used for drying certain leaves or finely cut vegetables, but Macaroni Products are a somewhat different proposition. The layer of material to be dried is much thicker, and the drying process is more than a simple dehydration. As a pre-Drier Infra Red can be used to good advantage, thus a battery of Infra Red Reflectors used in conjunction with a Sieve, as shown on page 123, would effect a very successful pre-drying.

High Frequency Heating

A source of energy that has great possibilities for drying Macaroni Products is high frequency heating. The general idea of working high frequency waves is very similar to Infra Red. The big advantage in favour of high frequency heating, however, is that it will readily penetrate into the core of the Macaroni Products even if they are handled in a thick layer, and then generate the heat exactly where it is required to evaporate the water inside the products.

Unfortunately, the quantities handled by the average Macaroni manufacturer require the installation of a very powerful plant generating high frequency energy, and such a plant is very expensive. Mainly for this reason no such high frequency Driers have yet been constructed.

Vacuum Drying

Vacuum has been used very successfully to dry a large variety of products, and has been used to dry Macaroni Products in half an hour, but the results have not been satisfactory. The drying is uniform and the products do not crack or break, but when cooked they prove to be of poor quality.

The quality can be brought back to the required standard if the drying operation is given the necessary time, but in this case any economical advantage which might be gained by the use of vacuum is lost.

Driers with Built-in Condensers

Driers of conventional design but using the drying air in a strictly closed circuit have been built, the idea being not to lose the heat contained in the air which in a normal Drier leaves with the exhaust, and which also carries away the evaporated water. It was further expected that in a strictly closed circuit it would be easier to regulate the temperature and the moisture of the drying air according to a pre-established diagram, thus obtaining perfect drying independent of outside conditions.

Circulation of the air in a strictly closed circuit made it necessary to extract part of the humidity contained in the air by passing the air over a Condenser, water being run through the Condenser to keep it at the required low temperature. Part of the moisture contained in the air will condense and can be evacuated as water. These Driers can give good results, but they are rather complicated in construction and operation. The water of condensation becomes contaminated by dust and dough, and causes endless difficulties. The use of Cabinet Driers with built-in Condensers has, therefore, been a very restricted one.

HANDLING DRIED MACARONI PRODUCTS

Short cut Macaroni Products if properly dried can be handled without any special care. They are hard and solid and will stand fairly rough usage, and may be conveyed by chutes, belts, and oscillating and pneumatic conveyors. They can be deposited in storage bins and packed by automatic packing machines, and may be handled in cotton or paper bags, small boxes or large containers.

Long Macaroni Products are much more delicate. They are as hard and solid as short cut products, but being long with a relatively small cross-section they break very easily. Long Macaroni Products must, therefore, be handled with great care on Belt Conveyors or in containers. Whenever possible Long Macaroni Products should be packed immediately they leave the Drier, and handled as finished packed goods. In many factories, as the Long Macaroni Products leave the Drier they are put into large boxes and the boxes carried to the packing room, but here a considerable proportion is broken as the goods are taken out of the box for final packing. This is almost inevitable as the long goods become intermingled very easily, and are broken when being separated. When weighing and packing the long Macaroni Products, advantage should be taken of the regular order in which they are deposited on the sticks in the Drier.

With a little care Noodles can be handled very much like short cut Macaroni Products, although they are more friable. Curls should not be mechanically handled, but should be taken from the Drier and packed by hand. The fine Vermicelli or Noodles from which these curls are mostly made are very brittle indeed, and will not stand up to normal mechanical handling.

CUTTING LONG DRIED MACARONI PRODUCTS

Long Macaroni and Spaghetti are generally cut after having been dried. There are two reasons for this, the first is to get rid of the U part or bend, which is formed when the fresh goods from the Press are put on to the sticks. The bends from Spaghetti that have been dried under perfect conditions are as good as any other part of the Spaghetti, but they do not make such a nice regular tight package as straight Spaghetti. If drying is not perfect and if wooden sticks have been used that are not perfectly clean, the bends will have a little more acidity than the remainder. This is particularly the case with Macaroni, and often a sufficient reason for eliminating the bend.

The other reason for cutting long Macaroni Products is that they are often distributed on the sticks twice as long as is required in the packet. It is more economical to dry the long Macaroni Products in lengths as long as possible without unduly stretching the fresh goods. Usual lengths are about 20 in. or in some cases even 30 in. The number of sticks to be handled for a given output is in reverse proportion to the length of the goods. Labour and cost of plant increases with the number of sticks which have to be handled, and therefore most fresh long Macaroni Products are 20 in. or more in length, despite the fact that a large proprtion is packed only 10 in. long. A 20 in. packet makes mechanical packing very difficult, and such packets are mostly only made for patrons who want to eat Spaghetti the Italian way, i.e. winding it up on a fork to a neat ball.

Long Macaroni Products are usually cut with a mechanically operated rotating saw, but ribbon saws are also used. Sometimes the products are broken by hand over a sharp edge.

Cutting dried Macaroni Products has always been an uneconomical operation. A lot of work is required to handle the long Macaroni Products and an uneconomical amount of splinters and broken pieces are produced.

In an effort to overcome these drawbacks Sarioni has devised a new and original cutting device. He takes advantage of the systematic order in which long Macaroni Products are arranged on the sticks for drying, and cuts the Spaghetti to the required length before it is taken off the sticks. On the Sarioni machine the sticks carrying the Spaghetti are fed into one end and carried through the machine by mechanical means. As they move through the machine circular saws cut the Spaghetti to the desired length and cut off the U part. The empty sticks and the cut Spaghetti come out separately at the discharge end of the machine.

The labour required to operate the Sarioni machine is about the same as would be necessary to take the dried Spaghetti off the sticks by hand, therefore practically the total amount of the labour required to cut the goods can be saved. Splinters and broken goods are about the same proportion as with a hand-fed circular saw. The Sarioni machine can be easily combined with a mechanical or a pneumatic transport system delivering the splinters and broken goods into a bin or directly into the hopper of a small grinding unit.

GRINDING DRY WASTE

Even the most efficient plant produces a certain amount of dry waste, i.e. short cuts that have been spilled, long goods that have been broken during handling, for instance, when they are taken out of the Drier, and the U bends and splinters produced when cutting the dried goods to the required length. Clean dry waste can be used for animal food. The bends of the Spaghetti and Macaroni are as good and nutritious as any other Macaroni Products, but as they lack any sales appeal they are often sold in bulk at a reduced price.

Most manufacturers of Macaroni Products refuse to sell a product not perfect in every respect, and it must be admitted that broken Macaroni Products do not look very appetizing. This factor has induced most manufacturers to grind the broken Macaroni Products that are not considered marketable to a fairly fine meal, very similar to ordinary Semolina, which is then incorporated into the Semolina and used for the manufacture of the cheaper grades. Impact Mills are generally used for this purpose. The only difficulty is in feeding the irregular and often cumbersome product to the Mill. Short cuts give no trouble, but broken long Spaghetti and Macaroni is a difficult problem and must be fed to the Mill by hand. A convenient Grinding unit with a special feeding device incorporated contains a large feed hopper with an oscillating wall. Large quantities of long Macaroni Products mixed with short cuts are filled into the feed hopper, the oscillating wall breaking the long goods into small pieces. These can then be fed by the rotating feeding device with the required regularity to the Impact Grinder, where they are ground into a fairly regular coarse meal.

CHAPTER VIII

THE QUALITY OF MACARONI PRODUCTS AND HOW IT CAN BE TESTED

CHARACTERISTICS OF GOOD MACARONI PRODUCTS

THE best Macaroni Products are smooth, translucent, hard, brittle and up to a point elastic, and they have a rich amber colour. Long pieces, particularly Spaghetti, are pliable and capable of withstanding considerable bending without breaking. When they break they show a clean, glassy fracture producing only a few pieces and no splinters.

Macaroni Products of inferior quality have a dull colour often with a shade of grey, sometimes they are almost dirty white. When made from very poor flour or handled on obsolete equipment they break unevenly with ragged edges, often producing objectionable splinters.

The final proof of the quality of Macaroni Products is in the eating, and the importance of the tests indicated above is because of their bearing on the cooking qualities of the products. When cooked, Macaroni Products swell and absorb water. Good products will absorb at least twice their weight of water, and swell to three or four times their original volume. They will retain their shape and a certain firmness, develop a clear appetizing odour, characteristic of hard wheat, and do not become pasty. When properly handled Macaroni Products do not lose their quality with storage, even over prolonged periods.

I know of Macaroni Products that have been kept for over ten years without any sign of deterioration. Stored in unsuitable conditions, for instance, in a warm, damp store-house, the best Macaroni Products will with time turn musty. This condition also follows inadequate drying, particularly if drying has been too slow at the beginning, or if the Macaroni Products have not been dried down to a moisture content of 13 per cent or less. Infestation with weevil and other insects is rather exceptional, as insects seldom get access to properly handled and well packed Macaroni Products.

Essential Conditions for the Production of Good Macaroni Products

First-class Macaroni Products can be made only from first-class raw materials. There is no doubt that good equipment and careful manufacture have an important bearing on the quality of Macaroni Products, but good raw materials are absolutely essential. This has been demonstrated in a most spectacular way during the late war. All manufacturers of Macaroni Products in Europe were compelled to use Semolina of inferior quality, and although some were using the very best equipment and experienced and reliable labour, they could not produce really first-class goods. First-grade Semolina, and if Noodles are made, first-grade Flour, are essential for producing the best-quality Macaroni Products.

The National Macaroni Manufacturers Association of U.S.A. define Semolina and Farina as follows:

"*Semolina* is the purified middlings obtained from the grinding of hard wheats otherwise known as Durum Wheat. It is free from bran and other offal and shall contain not more than 13·5 per cent moisture and not more than 1 per cent of flour.

"*Farina* is the purified middlings obtained from the grinding of hard wheats other than Durum Wheats. It is free from bran and other offal and shall contain not more than 13·5 per cent moisture and not more than 1 per cent of flour."

To ensure the use of regular quality Semolina, and this also applies to Flour as received from the Mill, all deliveries should be regularly controlled. Tests for moisture, ash, texture, and quantity of bran included should be regularly carried out, and the results kept on record. Where more than one grade of raw material is supplied, mixtures of different grades may be advisable to keep the quality of the Semolina as regular as possible. (*See* Blending of Semolina, on p. 28.)

The moisture content of the Semolina can be determined on the same apparatus as is used for testing the moisture content of finished products. The quantity of bran present is checked by measuring the ash content after treatment in a special oven, and by optical examination of the Semolina on a glass plate after it has been pressed with a flour spatula. If the glass plate with the Semolina is dipped in water and then left to dry, the difference in the purity of several grades will be seen much more clearly.

A regular check on the water used in the manufacture should be necessary only in exceptional cases. Average water supplies are so regular that once the water has been certified as being fit for human consumption, only occasional control tests will be necessary.

The Macaroni Products themselves must be controlled regularly during the manufacturing process, and control must start right at the beginning. It is essential to make a regular mixture of constant texture and humidity. This depends on the regularity of the Semolina, and of the flow of Semolina and water into the Mixer of the Continuous Extrusion Press, and should be controlled at regular intervals. After a few days training any average operative will be able to judge the mix by just looking at it and kneading it in his hand. The regularity of the mix can be improved by keeping a constant humidity in the closed Mixer. To effect this, it has been found to be an advantage to connect the lid of the Mixer with a small servo motor governed by a hygrostat inside the Mixer. If the air inside the Mixer gets too dry, the hygrostat will set the servo motor to close the lid of the Mixer completely. If the humidity inside the Mixer becomes too high, the lid is opened just a little, allowing fresh air access to the Mixer, and the humidity is then reduced. The same result may be achieved by using a small Fan to control the humidity inside the Mixer.

A good indication of the quality of the dough is given also by the ammeter connected to the motor driving the worm of the Continuous Extrusion Press. The power requirement of a modern Press is of remarkable regularity. When the Press is working under normal conditions, the ampere indicator is practically motionless. If the dough gets drier and harder, the power required will be greater and the ammeter will immediately indicate this increase. If the dough becomes softer, the ammeter will automatically register the lower power figure. The regularity of the dough may be kept within very close limits, if care is taken to ensure the indicator of the ammeter being kept within prescribed limits. This can be achieved by regulating the flow of Semolina and water accordingly. Using a registering ammeter a record can be kept of the power consumption of the Continuous Extrusion Press, and this record can be referred to at a later date if it should be necessary to check the quality of the goods produced at any particular time. Let us suppose that a customer has complained of having received rough short cut Elbows. By referring to the ammeter record for the day on which these Elbows were made, it may been seen that a peak load was registered, thus indicating that an exceptionally dry dough was produced resulting in Macaroni Products with a rough surface, and the complaint must be considered as justified.

If the Macaroni Products are smooth but have too much acidity and the ammeter records show an exceptionally low load, the goods were probably made too soft. The drying not having been set to take care of this abnormal situation, the Macaroni Products did not dry quickly enough and consequently too much acidity developed.

Alternatively, the ammeter may be combined with an alarm that will give a signal whenever the dough gets too hard or too soft. It has been suggested that an ammeter should be used in connection with the motor driving the Mixer in order to obtain an indication of the regularity of the mix. This could be an advantage as it is much easier to correct the mix than the dough. Unfortunately, the torque required to drive the continuous Mixer is so irregular that any indication derived from the motor driving the Mixer will be without value.

Once the dough has been extruded it should be inspected on the pre-Drier, for short cut goods, or during spreading if long Macaroni Products are produced.

During drying, the moisture content of the Macaroni Products must be controlled at regular intervals if efficient drying is to be obtained. Whatever the final moisture content of the finished goods is to be, they must all contain the same amount of moisture and be within about plus or minus 0·2 per cent of the prescribed figure. If goods are manufactured with varying moisture content, they will all have to remain in the Drier until those with the highest amount of moisture have been dried down to the required degree. This means that a certain proportion will have to be dried to a lower figure than is necessary, and a corresponding reduction in the yield will result. If this is not done some of the Macaroni Products will be insufficiently dried, and their keeping qualities will be impaired.

It is not sufficient to control only the moisture content of the finished products, as it is then generally too late to correct any mistakes that have been made. It is much better to measure the humidity of the Macaroni Products, say, every two hours, so as to check that the drying process is proceeding according to schedule. By this means any irregularity in drying will be noticed, and can be corrected in good time to prevent spoilage later on.

A quick and reliable instrument to determine the moisture content, should, therefore, be available in the Laboratory of every well-managed plant producing Macaroni Products.

After the finished Macaroni Products have been tested for general appearance, colour, texture, elasticity and smoothness, the final cooking test should be made. This will show how the Macaroni Products swell during cooking, how much water they absorb, how their texture is affected by prolonged cooking, how they taste, and how they smell.

Various types of apparatus, some of which will now be described, have been developed to make these different tests rapidly and with the required accuracy.

APPARATUS USED FOR TESTING SEMOLINA AND
MACARONI PRODUCTS

Moisture Test

Various methods are used to measure the moisture content of Semolina and Macaroni Products, two of which have gained major importance. The most direct and reliable one uses a sample of known weight which is heated to a standard temperature for a certain time; temperature and time depending on the apparatus used. During this heating period the sample loses its total amount of free water. If "A" is the weight of the sample before heating and "B" the weight after all the water has been evaporated, "A" minus "B" is the water contained in the sample, and $100 \dfrac{\text{"A"} - \text{"B"}}{\text{"A"}}$ is the moisture content in percentage as defined on page 19. If the weight of the sample

"A" is constant, it is possible to choose the graduation on the scale in such a manner that when the sample is weighed after complete dehydration, the humidity of the original sample can be read off on the dial directly in percentage.

An apparatus specially designed for the Macaroni Products industry, illustrated in Fig. 68, is supplied by Buhler Brothers.

Fig. 68.—Special Scale made by Buhler for testing the humidity of Macaroni Products.

This is provided with a tray about 12 in. diameter × ½ in. deep. The tray is placed on a support which is suspended from the arm of the scale. This tray is clearly visible in the illustration. The sample to be tested is ground to a coarse meal, and 10 grammes placed on the tray. The exact weight may now be checked by reading an illuminated scale at the left of the apparatus. After exactly 10 grammes have been filled into the tray, it is introduced into the electrically heated oven on top of the apparatus, and the sample desiccated for six minutes at a temperature of 130° C. When desiccation is complete, the weight of the tray, still in the oven, is shown on the scale by adjusting a lever, and the percentage of moisture is now shown on the dial. A sample can be tested by unskilled labour in a few minutes with an average accuracy of well within plus or minus 0·2 per cent.

Instead of weighing the completely dehydrated sample, it is also possible to condense the water evaporated from the sample and to weigh this, thus the difference "A" — "B" can be obtained directly. Braibanti are marketing an apparatus in which the water evaporated from the sample is condensed into a graduated tube. By always using a sample of the same weight the tube can be graduated so that the percentage of moisture may be immediately ascertained. This apparatus will give an accurate reading within ten minutes.

Another method in general use computes the moisture content by measuring the electrical conductivity of Semolina, or Macaroni Products ground to a coarse flour. The figures thus obtained are not quite so reliable as those obtained by weighing the sample before and after total dehydration, but they are, however, sufficiently accurate for most practical purposes. Results are obtained almost immediately, which makes this method very convenient. Various apparatus using this method have been designed. A construction by Kruger, of Switzerland, according to indications given by Eiken is connected to an electric light circuit, and the readings on the scale are compared with a graph. Thus, the percentage of moisture in the sample may be immediately ascertained.

Ash Test

The ash content is determined by heating a sample up to 1,100° F. Water and all organic matter are volatilized, leaving the ash, the weight of which can now be measured on a laboratory scale. The amount of ash is always very small when compared with the weight of the sample. It is, therefore, necessary to use a very accurate scale if reliable figures are to be obtained. The elimination of water and organic

Fig. 69.—Electric Furnace used for Ash Test.

matter must be complete. Special small furnaces have been designed for this purpose, the required heat being generated by electricity. An automatically controlled thermo-electric Ni-Ni Cr couple built into the base of the furnace, keeps the temperature inside the furnace to any figure between 80° and 2,000° F. The furnace is efficiently insulated which, combined with correct distribution of the heating coils, gives a very regular distribution of the heat and ensures consistent results of high accuracy. For average determinations the temperature is set at about 600° C. (1,112° F.), and the sample left in the oven for about 4 to 6 hours. When Macaroni Products are to be tested it is recommended that they be ground to a regular meal of a granulation similar to fine Semolina. Uniformity in the granulation will thus ensure all these tests being accurate and reliable. This is more particularly the case with the quick electric determination according to Eiken.

Cooking Test

The cooking test gives us information on the following most important points—how the Macaroni will stand up to cooking and in particular, how long it will retain its shape and firmness, how much water it will absorb, the increase in volume and weight, and how much of the substance is lost in the water in which the Macaroni is cooked. All this information can be obtained without any special apparatus, using only the utensils found in every kitchen.

Due to the importance of this test some devices have been developed to make the test easier and reliable. One of these is a set suggested by the Italian Professor Borasio. Macaroni Products must be cooked in boiling water in an open (uncovered) vessel. On an ordinary kitchen fire it will be next to impossible to keep the intensity of the boiling constant, and so get exactly the same boiling with each different test. The boiling water causes the Macaroni Products to be intensely agitated, and this agitation will depend on the intensity of the boiling and be different in each test, thus leading to results that are not strictly comparable. For this reason Professor Borasio has suggested that the vessel in which the Macaroni Products are cooked should be heated in an oil bath kept at about 218° F. (102° C.) by electric heating, thus the Macaroni Products are cooked at a constant temperature of about 208° F. (98° C.). The results of different tests are now strictly comparable and regular. It should be noted that the cooking time required by this apparatus is on an average two minutes more than will be required with freely boiling water.

It has been found convenient for routine control of quality to cook the sample to be tested in two vessels, cooking time in one case being 18 minutes, and 28 minutes in the other. After the Macaroni Products have been cooked the sample is left to drain on a sieve for five minutes and then weighed. The difference in weight between the cooked sample and the dry one gives the water absorption during cooking. By measuring the volume of the dry sample and the volume of the cooked sample with a volumeter, the increase in volume is easily computed. The water in which the samples have been cooked is placed in a graduated glass tube, and the suspension in the water left to settle for half an hour. After this time the water will have separated into two portions, being clear on top and milky at the bottom. The height of this milky section is a measure of the quantity of solid substance lost by the Macaroni Products during cooking.

The determination of the solid substance lost to water by measuring the sediment in the water used for cooking is not very accurate. For *prima vista* test this will be sufficient, but to obtain more accurate figures, 50 grammes of the cooking water, after this has been well stirred to give an even distribution of the solid content, should be placed in a small vessel and completely evaporated. The Scale illustrated on page 173 could be used for weighing the 50 grammes of cooking water. After complete evaporation the solid substance left is weighed, and its percentage may then be computed. For plain Macaroni Products, less than 6 per cent is very good, up to 8 per cent is average, and 10 per cent or more bad. If the cooking water test has been made with salted water, which gives a more reliable result, the corresponding amount of salt should be deducted when calculating the percentage of solid substance lost to water. The figures obtained will differ

Volume of 100 grammes of Macaroni Products in cm³	*85 cm³*	*92 cm³*	*85 cm³*	*87 cm³*	*87 cm³*	*95 cm³*
Cooking time	18 mins.	18 mins.	18 mins.	18 mins.	18 mins.	18 mins.
	28 ,,	28 ,,	28 ,,	28 ,,	28 ,,	28 ,,
Water absorbed in grammes	188	195	200	162	181	221
	260	235	260	200	237	284
Volume of cooked Macaroni Products in cm³	275	285	260	245	265	315
	350	335	350	305	330	370
Increase in volume	3·2	3	3	2·8	3·1	3·3
	4	3·6	4	3·5	3·8	3·9
Solid substance lost to water in percentages	5	6·2	4·6	5·8	5·5	8
	5·5	6·6	5·4	7	6·3	11·5
Cooking quality	very good	good	very good	average	good	bad

for the two samples, which have been cooked for 18 minutes and 28 minutes respectively. Considered together they will give a very reliable and constant indication of the quality of the Macaroni Products.

These indications can easily be put on record for future reference and comparison. The table on page 177 gives some figures published by Buhler of tests carried out on the Borasio Apparatus.

It must be remembered when making cooking tests, that Macaroni Products will behave differently according to their shape, size and thickness. When comparing, only figures relating to the same class of goods should be considered. For instance, Elbows of the same external and internal measurements, or Spaghetti of the same diameter, and so on. It is obvious that plain Macaroni Products will give different figures from Egg Macaroni Products, and a comparison of the figures obtained with Egg Macaroni Products with the figures given for plain Macaroni Products, will not be strictly true.

CHAPTER IX

STORING AND PACKING MACARONI PRODUCTS

STORING

PROPERLY dried, and stored in a cool, dry warehouse, Macaroni Products will keep for many years without losing any of their qualities. Given sufficient space, storage of Short Cuts is not a difficult problem. Before packing they can be stored for a short time in bins, boxes and containers. Bins and containers are generally arranged to provide an easy feed to the packing machine. Short Cuts that are to be stored for a prolonged period, up to a few years, are packed either in paper or cotton bags with capacities of from 50 to 100 lb., or in small $\frac{1}{2}$ lb., 1 lb. or 2 lb. sized packets.

Long Macaroni Products will keep just as well as short cuts, but should be stored only in their final packets. They are too friable to be conveniently handled in bulk, but once packed in 1 lb. or 2 lb. cartons, or in cardboard boxes of from 10 to 20 lb., they may be handled and stored quite easily. Latterly in Italy, long Macaroni Products, particularly Spaghetti, have been packed in large paper bags of square section, holding 50 lb. or more. The breakage of Spaghetti thus handled being much lower than might be expected.

PACKING

Macaroni Products are either sold in bulk, or packed in small packets of $\frac{1}{2}$ lb., 1 lb. or 2 lb. sizes. Short Cuts are more often sold in bulk, particularly in Southern Europe. Due to the shortage of packing materials during the war, increased quantities of Macaroni were sold in bulk or in large paper bags. In Italy, where large quantities of Spaghetti are consumed, it is still sold in large paper bags containing 10 and 20 lb. each, at the time of writing, and it is quite astonishing how well this Spaghetti will stand handling and transportation despite the rather crude packing.

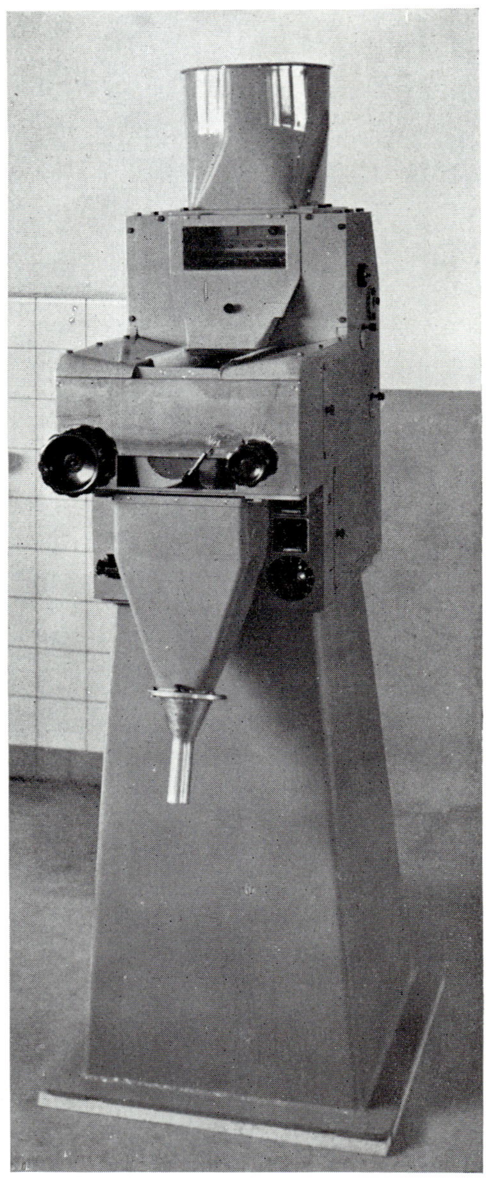

Fig. 70.—Weigher with a single spout made by S.I.G., capable of handling about 20 packages per minute.

In most countries where large quantities of Macaroni Products are bought, Short Cuts are sold in paper bags containing 10 to 20 lb. or even 50 lb., and long Macaroni Products in cardboard or wooden boxes of about the same capacities. The larger quantities are usually packed by hand. For packing Short Cuts in large quantities, a semi-mechanical device is often used. The Short Cuts coming from a storage bin or a large portable container run on to a vibrating Feeder, similar to the Soder Vibrator, page 76, and are delivered into a box or bag placed on an ordinary Scale. When the indicator on the Scale shows the correct weight, the vibrator on the Feeder is cut off and the feed stops immediately. The Scale is arranged to cut off the feed in time to include the relatively small quantity of goods which are between the Feeder and the packet. The indicator hand on the scale stops the feed, either by closing an auxiliary electric circuit, or by cutting of the light beam falling on a photo-electric cell.

Short Macaroni Products

Short cuts are usually packed in quantities of $\frac{1}{2}$ lb., 1 lb. and 2 lb., the two smaller sizes being most popular.

In most small plants producing Macaroni Products as a home industry small packets are filled by hand, but the majority of short cut products are handled on packing machines. These may be either a semi-automatic Weigher, or a fully automatic packing system. Semi-automatic Weighers are built by several firms; some measure the Short Cuts by volume but the more accurate method is by weight. They all have a vibrating feed tray into which the short cut goods are delivered either by a bucket conveyor, or direct from a storage bin. From the feed tray the goods flow into the bucket of the scale. When the required weight has been delivered to the bucket, the sinking movement of the scale cuts off the supply electrically, and the bucket discharges the weighed load into a bag or cardboard box placed under the filling spout by the operator. The vibration of the feed tray may be adjusted to suit the goods being handled, and to set the number of packets to be filled per minute. This number varies according to the type of machine. For a machine with one spout it is generally between 10 and 20 packets per minute. Installations with two or more spouts produce more in proportion to the number of spouts available. For average production and for goods that feed easily, single machines, are used. Whereas, for greater production, and at times for goods that do not flow easily, multiple machines are preferred. Such machines may be combined with a conveyor to carry the containers to a closing station after they have been filled. These machines handle bags as well as rigid containers.

For a greater output of one product, fully automatic packeting equipment has been built. With this equipment the cardboard boxes are glued, the goods weighed and filled into

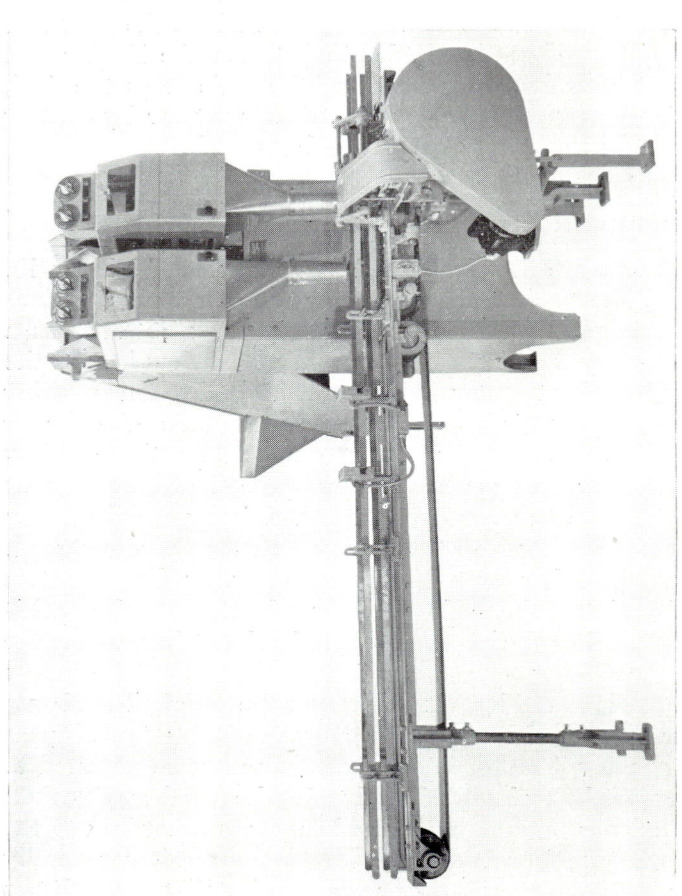

Fig. 71.—Triangle Automatic Packaging Line incorporating a double weigher, closing station and conveyor.

the boxes, the boxes closed, and then delivered either one by one, or in bundles of five or six or any other number required.

The illustration on page 184 shows a complete packing plant using four Weighers for an output of up to sixty packets per minute. The packets are made from pre-cut cardboard, and for additional protection are lined with paper taken from the roll on the left of the illustration. Transparent film and paper bags cannot be filled on this type of equipment. They are not as strong as cardboard containers, and generally are used as a substitute in places where the use of the more expensive cardboard boxes is prohibitive.

Long Macaroni Products

I have not described in detail the special machines used to make the containers into which Macaroni Products are packed, although these containers are generally made in every large Macaroni plant. These machines are not peculiar to the Macaroni Products industry, and are built in a large variety of different types and sizes. A detailed description would exceed the scope of this book, but they are to a large extent common to both long and short Macaroni Products.

The packing of long Macaroni Products can be divided into two distinct operations. First the Macaroni Products are weighed, and secondly, as an independent operation, the weighed bundles are packed into a suitable container or wrapped in paper or transparent film. The blue paper and red string originally used in Naples for wrapping long Spaghetti has acquired world wide fame, and in many cases the red string has been printed on cardboard containers to imitate this classic package.

The weighing of long Macaroni Products has always been a difficult operation. The main difficulty being to extract from a bulk of long Macaroni the exact quantity to be weighed. It is almost impossible to extract mechanically from a large container 1 lb. of Spaghetti or Macaroni. The individual strings of long Macaroni Products become intermingled when they are deposited in large quantities, and a certain amount is broken when a small quantity is picked up mechanically. For this reason it is generally done by hand. The machines used are designed to make this weighing operation as easy and

Fig. 72.—Fully automatic packaging line capable of an output of 60 packages per minute, built by S.I.G., Neuhausen, Switzerland.

efficient as possible. Once a bundle of long Macaroni Products having the required weight is prepared, it is easy to push the bundle into a suitable container or to wrap it into a roll.

Illustrated in Fig. 73 is a Weighing and Packing machine originally developed in Germany. The machine has two scales into which the required amount of long goods is fed by two girl operators. When the exact weight is obtained the scale tips, and the strings of Macaroni Products are brought together into a neat bundle and pushed into a container presented in front of the discharge spout by a third operative. The same operative can deal with both scales built into the machine, thus three operatives can handle 24 to 28 packets per minute. A machine built along these lines can be set to handle long Macaroni Products and scattered Noodles or similar types of goods.

A new and original approach to the problem of weighing long Macaroni Products has been suggested by Buhler. As already mentioned, the main difficulty is to segregate the required amount from a heap of long goods. Buhler eliminates this difficulty by taking advantage of the very regular order in which the long Macaroni Products are deposited on the sticks by their mechanical Spreader, and by counting the number of strings that go to make a packet of pre-determined weight. By correctly setting the Spreader and accepting a little more trimmings than is strictly necessary, all the strings of the product on the sticks can be made to have precisely the same length. By passing the sticks with the long goods through the Buhler Continuous Drier, all the strings of dough are dried to exactly the same moisture content. This means that the weight of the strings extruded through a certain number of holes will be constant. Holes in the Die are distributed to form a certain number of groups, the strings of long Macaroni Products extruded through each group of holes being of constant weight. On the sticks the strings are distributed in corresponding groups.

When the holes in the Dies become worn the diameter of the goods produced will increase, and the weight of each string will be greater. When this increase in weight is equal to the weight of one string of dried Macaroni Products, it can easily be compensated for by closing one of the holes of the group in the Die. In the Buhler Continuous Long Goods Drier, the strings of dough can be taken off the sticks

mechanically. The stripping apparatus can be arranged to
bundle the groups of long Macaroni Products, and to deposit
these bundles on a table or on a chain from which they can
be transferred into suitable containers either mechanically
or by hand.

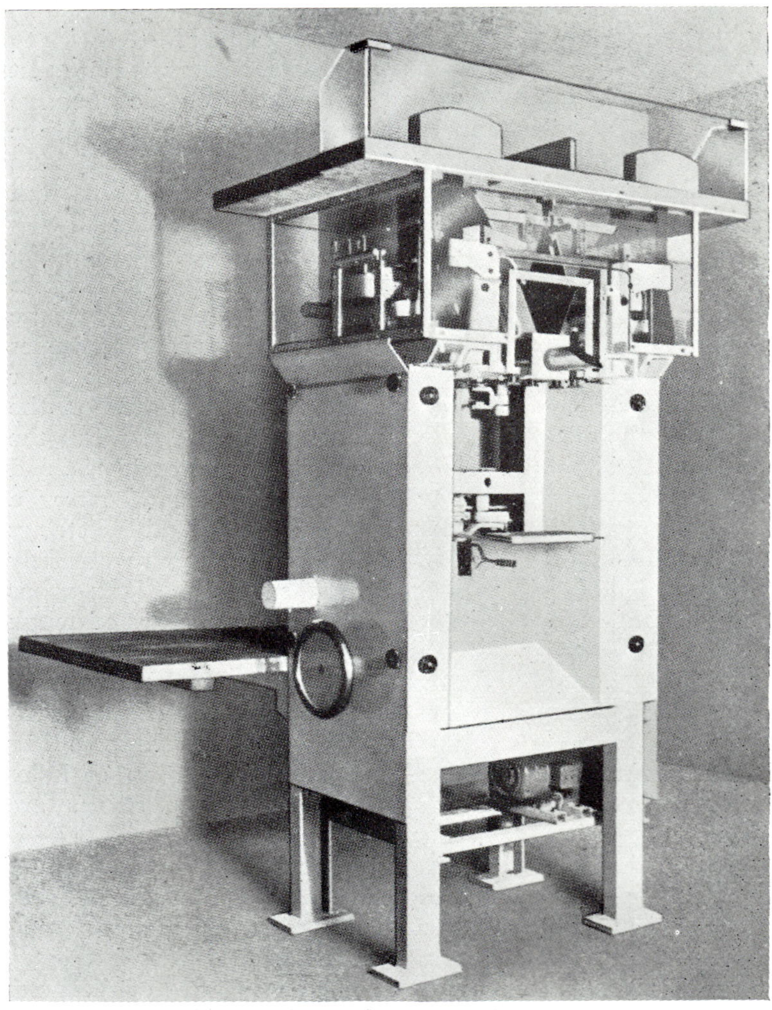

Fig. 73.—Weighing and Packing Machine for Long Macaroni
Products, manufactured by Blatter, Switzerland.

If the bends in the long Macaroni Products are to be eliminated or the Spaghetti broken into two halves, this can be done mechanically as the long Macaroni Products are taken off the sticks. The splinters and bends should be taken away by a Pneumatic Conveyor to ensure clean working of the machine, and deposited in a bin if they are to be sold separately, or fed directly into a Grinding Machine if they are eventually to return to the Extrusion Press.

CHAPTER X

THE IDEAL MACARONI PRODUCTS PLANT

BEFORE the Continuous Extrusion Press came into general use, the ideal plant worked as follows: Mixer, Gramola and Hydraulic Extrusion Press were disposed on three different levels, and the product worked from one machine into the other by gravity. Driers for long Macaroni Products

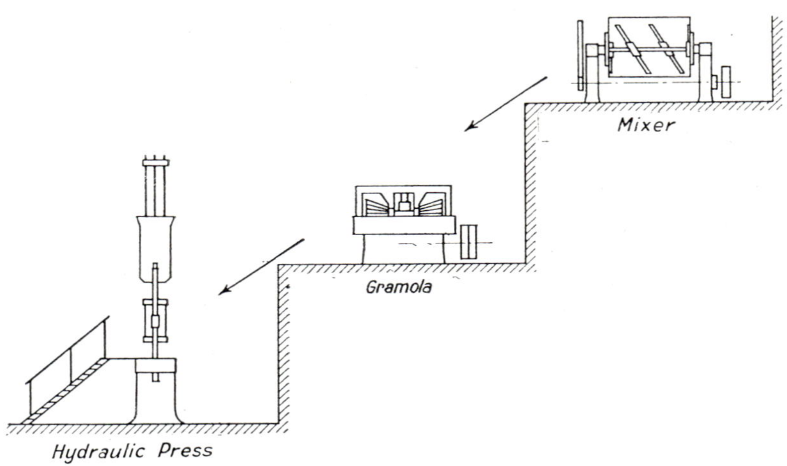

Fig. 74.—Working by gravity with Batch Machines.

used to be on the same floor as the Hydraulic Press, and short goods Driers on one or more floors above the Press. The products were generally packed on the upper floors and stocked on the lower, the despatch department being on the ground floor. As Mixers, Gramola and Hydraulic Presses have now been completely superseded by the modern Continuous Extrusion Press, there is no need to describe further a plant using these obsolete types of machines. I shall, therefore, consider a plant working with modern equipment designed for continuous operation, except for the Driers which may be of the batch or continuous type.

Some General Ideas

In the ideal plant, handling should be reduced to a minimum. It is much better to arrange the flow sheet of the plant in such a manner that transportation is not necessary, rather than have an ingenious and efficient transport system. If horizontal transport is bad, vertical transport is worse, and a really satisfactory layout should have no vertical transport of Macaroni Products, either fresh or dried, except by gravity.

Semolina will have to be lifted, and it makes little or no difference whether it is lifted one foot or thirty feet, therefore, the Continuous Extrusion Press should be erected on the top floor and all further vertical transport of the Macaroni Products executed by gravity. The operation of a modern Continuous Extrusion Press is very smooth, and setting up no vibration or excessive load, it can be safely disposed on the upper floor of any industrial building.

The extruded Macaroni Products, both long and short, are delicate and difficult to handle before they are dried, and, therefore, should be conveyed on the shortest possible route. This means that the long goods Driers should in any case be on the same floor as the Presses. Once they are dried, Macaroni Products can be handled with ease. They can now pass to the lower floors by gravity without any difficulty if a two-storey building is used, or conveyed horizontally to the packing room if the plant is to be on one floor. Storage and despatch should be on the ground floor, and the height of the floor above street level arranged to suit the height of the wagons or railway cars into which the goods are to be loaded.

Small and average sized plants will find it an advantage to receive the Semolina and despatch the finished goods on the same side of the building, which will make supervision easy. For larger plants this will not always be the case, as in such plants the incoming products and the outgoing goods are in such quantities that there should be no cross-traffic. The size of such plants will justify one control for the reception of the raw material, and one for the despatch of the finished goods.

A Small Plant, 6,000 lb. per day

The diagram overleaf shows a plant to handle about 6,000 lb.

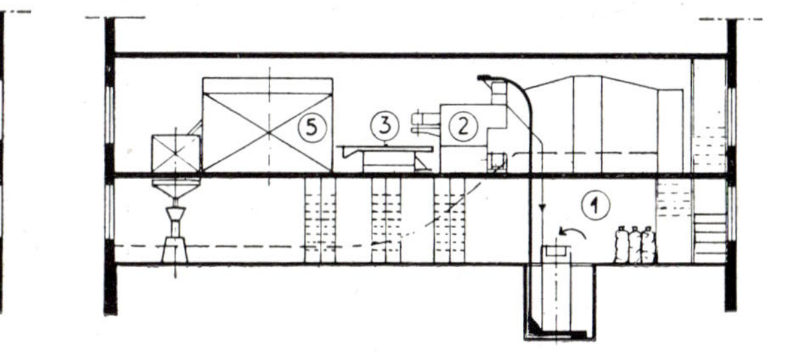
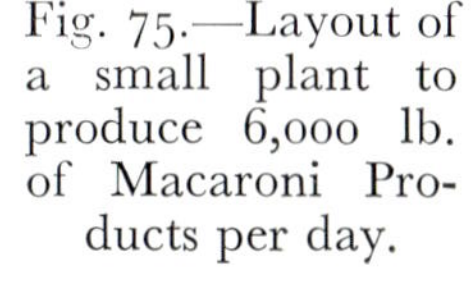

Fig. 75.—Layout of a small plant to produce 6,000 lb. of Macaroni Products per day.

KEY

1. Semolina Intake.
2. Continuous Extrusion Press.
3. Pre-Drier.
4. Oscillating conveyor for short cut goods.
5. Short cut goods Drier.
6. Weigher for short goods.
7. Spreader for long Macaroni Products.
8. Driers for long Macaroni Products.
9. Stock.
10. Dies.
11. Die Washing Machine.
12. Opening for lifting machinery.
13. Laboratory Superintendent.
14. Office accommodation.

of Macaroni Products per day, with 8 hours production on the Press and 24 hours for the Driers. The sacks of Semolina are received in a special room, where they are stored and emptied into the receiving hopper. Cotton and jute sacks are immediately cleaned and folded ready for return to the Mill. Paper bags should be disposed of immediately, thus, no bags or sacks, the usual source of infestation, go into the plant itself.

From the receiving hopper the Semolina passes over a control sieve, and is elevated by a chain type Conveyor into the receiving spout of the Continuous Extrusion Press. As it is almost impossible to set a chain Conveyor to carry the exact amount required, it must be set to carry more Semolina than is required by the Press and the excess returned direct to the receiving hopper by means of a chute.

If blending of Semolina is carried out, it will be convenient to divide the receiving hopper and the control sieve into two sections, and to use a double chain conveyor to carry both types of Semolina to the Press. One type going to each feeding system built into the Continuous Extrusion Press, and thus blending the Semolina by setting each feeding system accordingly. Two separate chutes must be provided to return the excess Semolina to the correct side of the hopper.

From the Continuous Extrusion Press, Short Cuts are received on a pre-Drier, and delivered directly to the short goods Drier by an Oscillating Conveyor. This Drier will comfortably accommodate 1,600 lb. of average short cut goods, and will dry all types of Short Cuts in a maximum time of 18 hours. For small short cut goods the drying time is considerably less. For the production considered there is no point in taking advantage of a possible short drying time, as it will be more convenient to fill the Driers once a day only, and not run the Extrusion Press longer than the regular eight hour shift.

For the production of long Macaroni Products, a special fitting is inserted in the Extrusion Press where the die is normally located. This special fitting connects the Press with a long goods Spreader, which spreads the long goods on sticks and automatically returns the trimmings to the Mixer of the Press. The sticks with the long goods are fed into the long goods Drier by hand. A long goods Drier will normally accommodate about 3,000 lb. of long goods. If easily dried long goods are produced, for instance, fine or medium Spaghetti and Vermicelli, they can be dried in less than 24 hours, making it possible to fill the Drier every day. If, however, Macaroni and heavy Spaghetti are produced, the Drier can be filled at the most only twice in three days. If the plant is to work comfortably with a steady production of 3,000 lb. of Short Cuts and 3,000 lb. of long goods per day, two long goods Driers should be provided.

The dried short goods coming from the Drier fall on to an Oscillating Conveyor and are delivered into one of a set of three to five bins, the number of bins depending on the variety of goods produced.

A Weigher is fitted on rails under the bins, thus enabling it to be connected to any of the bins. The short cut goods are weighed and filled into containers which are sealed by hand, and then carried to the stores or despatch room on trolleys.

The long goods are weighed and packed by hand on tables on the same floor as the Drier. The relatively small capacity will not warrant any mechanical Weighing or Packing Machines for long goods. The packed goods slide down to the store or despatch department.

A separate room is provided close to the Extrusion Press for washing and storing the dies, and for preparing the egg mixture if egg Macaroni Products are to be produced. Adequate Office accommodation, together with a small Laboratory combined with a Superintendent's room, must be provided according to individual needs.

The production of such a plant can easily be increased by installing more Driers, and running the Press more than eight hours a day. It will be wise to reserve the necessary space for extra Driers right from the start, thus ensuring that it will not be necessary to modify the conveyors, bins and packing room at a later date. The layout of this plant does not include the installation of further Extrusion Presses, and should this be necessary the general disposition should be that of a small plant arranged on two floors. This plant may be easily installed on one floor, by using a bucket elevator to carry the short cut products coming from the Drier to the bins.

A Large Plant, 60,000 lb. per day

For large outputs, continuous Driers for long and short cut goods must be used. It will be advisable to use a separate Drier for each Continuous Extrusion Press, thus reducing changing and resetting of the machines to a minimum. Continuous Extrusion Presses running 24 hours a day have an average output of 20,000 lb. each, and the Driers should be built to handle this quantity. This leads to the installation of a production unit producing as an average 20,000 lb. of finished goods per day. If Macaroni Products requiring a large number of sticks are made, for instance, fine Spaghetti, the output will be less, as there will not be sufficient sticks available in the Drier to accommodate 20,000 lb. The output of the production unit is in this case limited by the Drier. If heavy Macaroni is made, substantially more than 20,000 lb. could be spread on the sticks, in which case the output of the Extrusion Press will be the limiting factor. In most cases it will be convenient to run the Driers at a definite speed. The output of the Continuous Extrusion Press will then have to be synchronized with the output of the Drier. As this will vary with the size of the goods produced, a variable speed motor should be used to run the Press.

If it is essential to produce about 20,000 lb. of heavy and light long goods per production unit, the speed of the sticks going through the Drier may be varied by using a variable speed drive on the Drier. When heavy Macaroni Products are produced, the loaded sticks will travel slowly through the Drier allowing them the time required to dry properly. The speed will be set to a point when the total possible production of the Extrusion Press can be absorbed on the sticks. When manufacturing light Macaroni Products, advantage may be taken of the possibility of drying such products in a shorter time by running the sticks through the Drier at a higher speed. A larger number of sticks will now go through the Spreader per hour, and, although each stick will carry less weight of long goods, the larger number of loaded sticks will make it possible to use the Extrusion Press to full capacity, the limit of the production unit now being set by the extrusion speed.

What has been said regarding long Macaroni Products

M

applies equally to short cut goods. Variations with Short Cuts are less than with long goods. With long goods the number of strings on each stick is strictly limited, whereas with Short Cuts, the thickness of the layer of goods on the drying conveyor may vary within fairly large limits without drawback, and thus compensate to a great extent any small difference in the weight per cu. ft., which determines the quantity of products that the Drier will hold. With Short Cuts the output of the production unit can be kept fairly constant for most types of goods, and is limited by the output of the Press and the size of the Drier. An output of about 20,000 lb. per day seems a convenient size for large plants. A smaller quantity will increase the initial cost considerably, and a larger amount will require more frequent changes of the die, and will, in most cases, not be economic except where very large quantities of the same goods are produced. Even if a plant is started with the object of manufacturing a certain size of Macaroni Product in very large quantities, it does not seem advisable to choose too specialized a layout. Conditions may change, and a plant capable of an economical production of a fairly large variety of products is always to be preferred.

Semolina is received in sacks or bags or in large containers and delivered into the receiving hopper. No bags or sacks are allowed inside the plant. From the intake hopper the Semolina runs over a control sieve, and is conveyed from there to the bins by pneumatic conveyors. These conveyors have been designed by Buhler especially for the Macaroni Products industry, and they are by far the cleanest and most efficient way of conveying Semolina in large quantities. The smooth seamless steel tubes, through which the Semolina is passed, can be kept perfectly clean with ease. The danger of insects breeding in deposits of Semolina, which is always present in bucket elevators or screw conveyors, is entirely eliminated. Air and Semolina are separated in a special cyclone. The Semolina going to a bin, and the air either to a filter or back into the pneumatic system. As a rule four to six bins are provided, which enables the necessary elasticity in the intake of the Semolina and the feed to the Press. In most countries two grades of Semolina are used, and at least four bins should be provided to take care of both grades of Semolina independently.

The Semolina should be extracted from the bins by a Mixer, as this is practically the only machine which will extract all types of Semolina and Flour. If only Semolina is used, such an elaborate arrangement is not necessary as Semolina flows quite freely. The majority of Macaroni Products manufacturers all over the world have had to use flour that will not flow easily, and have experienced quite a lot of trouble in extracting this flour from the bins.

One Extrusion Press is combined with a Spreader and a Continuous Long Goods Drier for a production unit with an average capacity of 20,000 lb. per 24 hour day. The finished packed long Macaroni Products slide down to the ground floor for storage or despatch. A second Extrusion Press works in conjunction with a Continuous Short Goods Drier, which will handle the 20,000 lb. extruded by the Extrusion Press running night and day. The dried short cut goods go into bins, and are packed from the bins on a fully automatic packing line, The long goods have to be packed as they leave the Drier, and that means a 24 hour day for packing. This is a disadvantage as night work in the Packing Department should be eliminated as far as possible. Large packets of 10 lb. or more that can easily be packed from the Drier by a single operative, should, therefore, be made during the night shift, and the smaller packets requiring more personnel should be produced during the day. With short cut goods this problem does not arise, as they can be sent into the bins during the night hours and packed in the normal working day. The automatic packing line should, therefore, be installed to handle 20,000 lb. in eight hours.

The third Extrusion Press is fitted with a Noodle sheet die, and produces a sheet of dough which passes to a set of Dough Breakers combined with a Noodle Cutting Machine. After running over a Noodle pre-Drier the Noodles go to a Continuous Drier, and the finished Noodles are then delivered to storage bins. From these bins the Noodles go to automatic Noodle Packing Equipment having a sufficient capacity to handle the total production in eight hours. Specialities and small products, which as a rule are produced in small quantities, are made on a fourth Press in the usual way, they pass over a pre-Drier and then go to Batch Driers. From the Batch Driers the dried goods go to storage bins. A single Weigher should be sufficient in most cases to handle the comparatively small quantities of goods and specialities that are manufactured during the day shift.

The layout foresees the possibility of increasing capacity, and provides necessary space for washing and storing the dies, handling the eggs, and installing the laboratories to ensure sufficient control of the raw product and manufactured goods. Storage and despatch rooms can be indicated only very approximately as they may vary very considerably according to local conditions and selling organization. The same may be said of office facilities.

It will be noticed that no special provision has been made for the heating of the Drier, but the most convenient and efficient heating is by electricity. Electrical heat is generally more expensive per B.T.U. than heat generated by gas, coal or oil, but if proper allowance is made for the simplicity of the electrical installation, and the clean and easy manner in which it operates, in most cases it will be a distinct advantage to provide a new plant with electrical heating of the Driers. If electricity is to be used for heating the building itself, this question must be settled separately according to local conditions. When electric heating is not available, or too expensive, it is possible to heat the Driers with hot water or steam.

In certain cases a mixed heating will be more economical and yet fairly convenient. The bulk of the heat 60–80 per cent is conveyed to the Drier by hot water, and only the remainder which requires accurate setting is generated by electricity. I shall refer in more detail to this problem in the chapter devoted to the theoretical side of drying Macaroni Products.

CHAPTER XI

NOTES ON THE THEORY OF DRYING

BEFORE discussing in detail the theory of drying Macaroni Products we must ensure that we are conversant with some basic thermodynamic facts.

Pure air per unit will hold as vapour a quantity of water which depends on the relative humidity, the pressure and temperature of the air. The relative humidity of perfectly dry air is "O" and this air contains no water at all. If the relative humidity is 100 per cent, the air contains the maximum amount of water vapour that it will hold, this amount depending on the air pressure and temperature.

The amount of water contained in 1 kg. of pure air at different temperatures and relative humidities, is to be found in tables published in current text books on thermodynamics or in graphs. Graph 1 established for air under normal pressure shows as X the quantity of water in grammes contained in 1 kg. of pure air. The curves of even temperature in ° C. The curves of even relative humidity (symbol η):

$\eta = 1$ means air having a relative humidity of 100 per cent or 1.

$\eta = 0.5$ means a relative humidity of 50 per cent or 0.5 and so on.

the curves Xs—X in grammes per kg. of pure air, Xs being the water contained in the air at saturation point, X the water effectively contained in the air under consideration.

Xs—X shows the quantity of water that the air can absorb before being saturated.

the curves i, i being the heat measured in kg. calories per kg. of pure air, it includes the heat contained in the vapour carried by the air.

This Graph answers all questions relating to the amount of water or heat contained in a certain quantity of air and how this varies under changing conditions. For example, let us consider air at 30° C. and with a relative humidity of 50 per

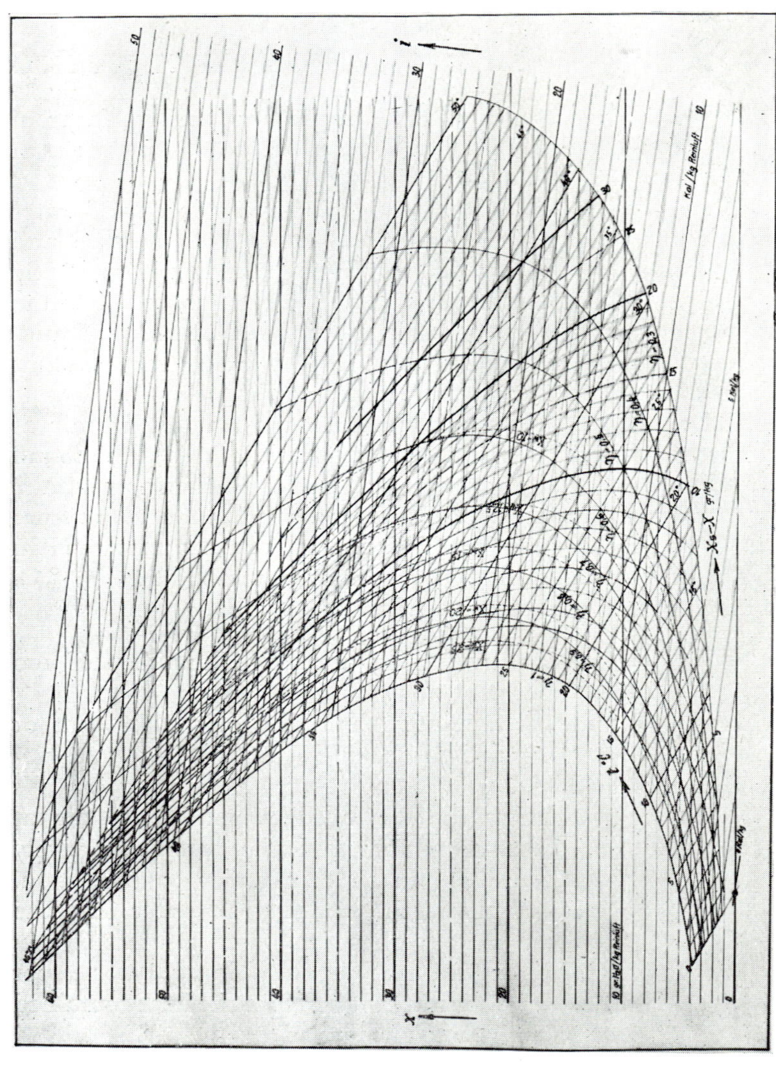

Graph I.

cent. By following the temperature curve $t = 30$ to its intersection A with the relative humidity curve $\eta = 0.5$. To point A corresponds $X = 13.4$ grammes of water per kg. of pure air being the water contained in the air as vapour, and $i = 15.3$ kg. calories per kg. of pure air, this being the heat contained in the air, if we consider the heat contained in the air at $t = 0$ $\eta = 0$ to be $i = 0$. As we shall never deal with air having a temperature below $0°$ C. and shall always deal with differences of i, this assumption is acceptable. If we now ask what is the maximum amount of water that could just be held by 1 kg. of pure air at $30°$ C., we follow the temperature curve $t = 30$ to its intersection with $\eta = 1$ and read $X = 27$ grammes.

If the values obtained on the Graph are compared with the figures given in a table it must not be forgotten that Graph 1 can give only approximate figures and for practical purposes these are of quite sufficient accuracy.

The evaporation of water on a tranquil water surface exposed to the air is governed by the formula of Dalton:

$$(1) \quad Q = C \ S \frac{\xi \ (t') - h}{H} \ Z$$

in which Q is the quantity of water evaporated;
C a coefficient depending on the agitation of the air;
S the surface of the water exposed to the air;
$\xi \ (t')$ the pressure of the vapour on the water surface at the temperature t';
h the mean vapour pressure in the air;
H the barometric pressure; and
Z the time.

If we consider the schematic extract taken from Diagram Graph 1 and shown overleaf, it can be seen that:
(Formula of Sprung)
$$(2) \quad \xi \ (t') - h = 0.5 \ (t - t')$$

and equation (1) can be written:

$$(3) \quad Q = C \ S \ \frac{0.5 \ (t - t')}{H} \ Z \ \text{for } t = t', \ Q = 0$$

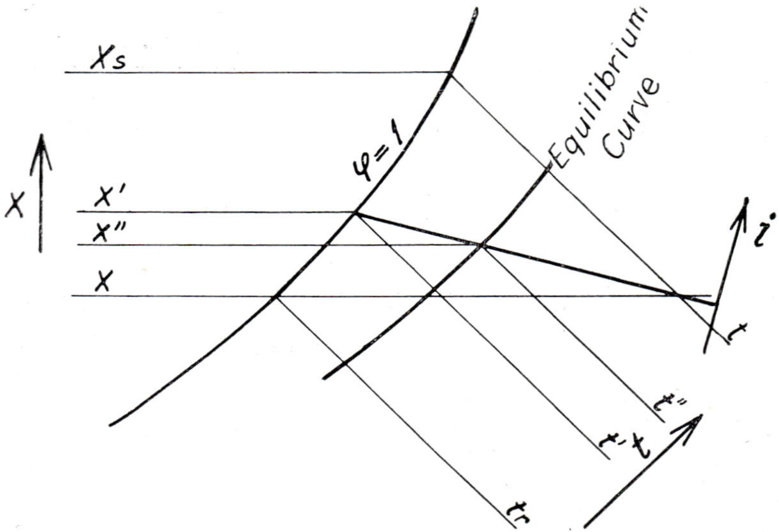

Fig. 77.—Extract from Diagram Graph I.

no water is evaporated, we have equilibrium between the water and the air. This is exactly what the diagram shows, for $t = t'$ we have $\eta = 1$ which means that the air is saturated and will therefore absorb no further water.

When considering Macaroni Products we assume that the quantity of water evaporated from the Macaroni Products will be governed by equation (3) in which t' will have been replaced by t'', t'' corresponding to the temperature of the air that would be in equilibrium with Macaroni Products having the temperature and the relative humidity considered.

In the above diagram the curves t'' have been drawn using figures obtained by Schlumpf.

These curves show temperature and relative humidity of air in equilibrium with Macaroni Products of a given humidity. For $t = t''$ no water is evaporated from the Macaroni Products. If t is greater than t'' the air will absorb water from the Macaroni Products and they will dry. If t is smaller than t'' the contrary will happen, the Macaroni Products will absorb water from the air and their moisture content will increase.

The first case corresponds to the evaporation of water on a free water surface, if the surrounding air is not saturated, the second case to condensation if the air is cooled below dew point.

Considering equation (3) in which for Macaroni Products t' is replaced by t'', it is possible to calculate the water evaporated from Macaroni Products by air of known temperature and relative humidity, as in the Driers used in the Macaroni Products industry, the heat contained i, as we shall see later, remains constant. In equation (3) t and t'' vary with Z, if this is properly considered equation (3) leads to a differential equation which involves calculations that are beyond the scope of this book. It must further be considered that the coefficient C for Macaroni Products is not well known which is a further difficulty in dealing with equation (3). Fortunately, there is another easy approach to the problem that involves only simple calculation if proper use is made of Graph 1. First let us see exactly what is the meaning of i, the heat contained per kg. of pure air.

As we shall not have to deal with air below $0°$ C., we consider i as being the heat which is brought into the air if its temperature is increased from 0 to t, and its water content from 0 to X. Therefore, we have:

$$i = C_1 + C_2 X$$

C_1 being the specific heat of air at constant pressure and C_2 the heat contained in one gramme of water vapour at the pressure under consideration and the temperature t.

The values of i are shown in Graph 1.

Reverting to our previous example $t = 30°$ C. $\eta = 0.5$ point A in Graph 1 reads $i = 15.3$ kg. calories per kg. of pure air.

Changes of pressure, temperature and humidity in the air are known as adiabatic if i remains constant. On the Graph 1, which I must repeat, presumes constant normal atmospheric pressure, this means that the point representing the condition of the air, moves along a curve of constant i. I shall now show that the changes of the air within the normal Drier can be considered as adiabatic.

This is only true for the normal Drier in which all the heat is brought into the Macaroni Products by air that has been heated, for instance, on an Air Heater, which, for our calculation does not belong to the drying zone. Driers working with Infra Red or High Frequency and thus introducing heat directly into the Macaroni Products, will have to be calculated in a similar but slightly modified manner.

In the normal Drier air of known temperature t, and water content X, is brought into contact with the Macaroni Product and leaves the active zone of the Drier at a temperature t* and a water content X*. t* is lower than t, which means that the air has lost some of its heat. We shall now see where this heat has gone. To start with part of the heat has been used to heat the Macaroni Products. If we figure that Macaroni Products have entered the Drier at 20° C. and attain 40° C. as maximum temperature, the specific heat of Macaroni Products being about 0·4, kg. Calories/kg. ° C., the heat required to heat 1 kg. of Macaroni Products from 20° C. to 40° C. will be $(40 - 20) \times 0.4 = 8$ kg. calories. Compared with the heat required to evaporate the water that has to be driven out of the Macaroni Products, this figure is so small that we shall disregard it in our further calculations. The error is further reduced when the total drying period is considered, as part of the heat is recuperated in the last drying hours the Macaroni Products leaving the Drier at practically the same temperature as they entered it.

To produce 1 kg. of dried Macaroni Products with a moisture content of 13 per cent, about 0·25 kg. of water must be evaporated at an average temperature of $\dfrac{40 + 20}{2} = 30°$ C.

It takes 580 kg. calories to evaporate 1 kg. of water under these conditions and therefore $0.25 \times 580 = 145$ kg. calories to evaporate the 0·25 kgs. of water that have to be extracted from the Macaroni Products.

A small part of the heat is lost by conductibility and radiation to the environment. This will particularly be the case on the exterior walls. Inside the active zone of the Drier where the Macaroni Products are in contact with the drying air, such losses are negligible and need not be considered. Setting up the thermic balance sheet of the Drier it can easily be shown that with a properly constructed unit the total thermic efficiency, which shows the total loss of heat through the external walls, is above 90 per cent. If the total loss of heat is less than 10 per cent, the heat lost inside the active zone where the air blows through the Macaroni Products, is much less and can safely be disregarded.

For our calculation we may therefore consider that the total amount of heat liberated by cooling the drying air over the Macaroni Products is used to evaporate water from the Macaroni Products. Now this vapour goes into the drying air and increases its X and therefore its i by exactly the same quantity as its i has been decreased by cooling. In other words, by contact with the Macaroni Products to be dried, the air changes its condition adiabatically, i remains constant. With Graph 1, we can now answer practically all the thermodynamic questions arising in drying Macaroni Products.

For example, if the drying air initially at $t = 30°$ C. and $\eta = 0·7$ goes over the Macaroni Products and leaves them at $28°$ C., how much water has been evaporated per kg. of pure air? Graph 1 gives for $t = 30$ $\eta = 0·7$ $X = 18·8$ grammes. We can now follow the corresponding i curve to its intersection with the curve $t = 28°$ C. and find $\eta = 0·82$ and $X = 19·8$. About 1 gramme of water has been evaporated for 1 kg. of drying air.

If the section of the Drier under consideration contains 200 kg. of wet Macaroni Products, and if we require to reduce the moisture content of these Macaroni Products by 3 per cent, 3 kg. of water have to be evaporated for every 100 kg. of Macaroni Products. We shall therefore have to evaporate a total of 6 kg. of water. As 1 kg. of air carries away 1 gramme of water, 6,000 kg. of air will have to be blown through the Macaroni Products. Table 1 shows that at $30°$ C. 1 kg. of saturated air has a volume of $0·896$ m³.

With $\eta = 0·7$ instead of $0·896$, the volume of 1 kg. of pure air is a little smaller, the exact figure being

$$\frac{0·76\ (1\ +\ 0·00367\ t)\ \text{m}^3}{1·293\ (0·76\ -\ \xi\ (t))}$$

t being the temperature of the air and ξ (t) the pressure of the water vapour at the temperature t.

For the practical purpose of finding the size of the Fan necessary to give the required amount of air, the figures given in Table 1 are quite sufficient.

TABLE I

SPECIFIC VOLUME OF HUMID AIR AS COMPARED WITH
1 KG. OF PURE AIR

TEMPERATURE	RELATIVE HUMIDITY				
	100%	90%	80%	70%	60%
° C.	m³/kg.	m³/kg.	m³/kg.	m³/kg.	m³/kg.
10	0·812	0·811	0·810	0·809	0·808
15	0·830	0·829	0·828	0·826	0·825
20	0·850	0·848	0·846	0·844	0·842
25	0·872	0·869	0·866	0·863	0·860
30	0·896	0·892	0·888	0·885	0·881
35	0·924	0·918	0·913	0·908	0·903
40	0·957	0·949	0·942	0·935	0·928
45	0·995	0·985	0·975	0·965	0·955
50	1·042	1·027	1·014	1·000	0·987

In none of our calculations have we taken into consideration the time factor. From a purely thermodynamic point of view, as illustrated in Graph 1, the time factor is of no importance. If we cool the drying air by passing it over the Macaroni Products, the heat thus introduced into the Drier will evaporate a certain amount of water whether we introduce it quickly or slowly. We have seen previously that the time required to dry Macaroni Products has an important bearing on the quality of the finished product, and we must now see how we can introduce this very important time factor into our calculations.

To introduce the time factor we must find what I shall call the Drying Curve. On the horizontal we figure the time, on the vertical the percentage of water contained in the Macaroni Products. The Curve as shown in the diagram shows us that the drying started with Macaroni Products containing 31 per cent of water, the water content dropped in 24 hours to 13 per cent, the rate of dropping being indicated by the Curve. The Drying Curve that will give the best results in a given case must be established empirically, as there are too many factors involved that cannot be worked out by mathematics.

Once the best Drying Curve has been found all that will be necessary is to reproduce this Curve in the Drier with the required regularity. This can be done by noting temperature, relative humidity and quantity of air blown through the Macaroni Products at every moment when the drying Curve is established, and by reproducing these factors as accurately as possible in the Drier. This means that we shall have to pass air through the Macaroni Products at a specified speed, temperature and relative humidity. In practice the speed of the air is kept fairly constant and is determined by the

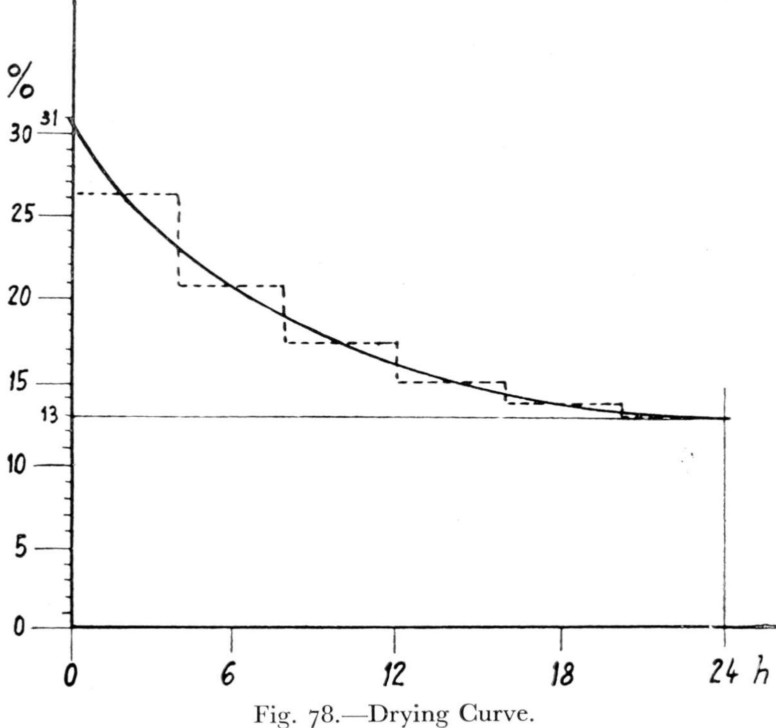

Fig. 78.—Drying Curve.

Fan. Temperature and moisture are controlled by thermometer and hygrometer, or psychrometer, if setting of the Drier is made by hand, and by thermostat and hygrostat for Driers with mechanical control.

The Drying Curve may also be used to indicate directly

the amount of water that has been evaporated, and thereby the necessary amount of heat introduced into the Drier.

The Drying Curve now tells us how much heat we must introduce into the Macaroni Products at any moment to reproduce the Drying Curve. If we multiply this heat by an experimental factor, taking care of the loss of heat through the walls of the Drier and eventually through the exhaust, we find the amount of heat that has to be supplied to the Drier. The setting of this heat is particularly easy and reliable if we use electric Air Heaters.

If we replace the Drying Curve by a broken line, each horizontal section representing a section of a Continuous Drier, the vertical corresponding to each horizontal line gives us directly the power of the heating unit to be built into each section of the Drier. It will be noted that temperature and relative humidity of the air have dropped out. If the correct amount of heat is introduced they will adjust themselves automatically to reproduce the Drying Curve with an accuracy sufficient for all practical purposes, so long as the fresh air introduced into the system is of reasonable quantity, temperature and moisture. Such a Drier can therefore be worked without consulting thermometer and hygrometer, and does not require an air conditioned room.

If hot water is used to introduce the heat, adjustment of the heat is a little more difficult than with electricity. The transmission of heat will in this case depend on the difference between the temperature of the hot water and the temperature of the air going over the Air Heater.

Where electricity is expensive, combined heating might be considered. The bulk of the heat could be introduced into the system at the beginning of the drying period and may be brought in by hot water, the final adjustment being made during the second half of the drying time by electric heating, which is easily adjustable.

It will always be advisable to keep a check on how the drying proceeds by testing the moisture content of the Macaroni Products at regular intervals, and comparing the figures obtained with the Drying Curves. Thus any deviation from the Drying Curve will be noticed in sufficient time for eventual correction.

The heat to be introduced is in direct proportion to the

weight of Macaroni Products contained in the Drier. This
weight varies with different types of Macaroni Products. It
is, for instance, very different for heavy Macaroni as compared with light fine Spaghetti. Heating must be adjusted
according to the type of goods being dried. On a Continuous
Drier this heat adjustment can be eliminated in most cases
by running the conveying chain at different speeds for different
products. The speed is selected in such a way that the same
weight of Macaroni Products always passes through a drying
section in a given time. In this case drying time for light
products will be shorter than the drying time required for
heavy goods, a condition that is quite compatible with the
manufacture of first-class products. Adjusting the speed of the
Continuous Drier is easy and well justified by an increased
output on light products.

If we revert to our fundamental equation (1) we find that
the evaporated water is proportional to the surface exposed
to the drying air. This explains the well-known principle of
gently shuffling Short Cuts, and the beneficial effect of a
blast of air strong enough to slightly move long goods as
they hang on sticks in the Drier. Where long goods stay in
permanent contact in a fixed position during drying, the drying
time must be increased to allow for adjustment of the moisture
inside the goods and thus prevent cracking and breakage.
This is one of the reasons why long goods take such a long
time to dry in most Cabinet Driers, and why Macaroni can
be dried in 24 hours on the Yberty Drier where the air is
blown through the hole so that contact between the Macaroni
does not interfere with the drying.

On Continuous Driers where a short drying time is of
particular economical importance, long goods should be
spread on the sticks with a sufficient space between the strings
for each string to be completely isolated so that it can be
surrounded by drying air.

Graph 2 gives us the answer to the following question.
Using Semolina with 15 per cent of moisture and adding
25 kg. of water per 100 kgs. of Semolina, what is the moisture
content of the mixture? From the 0 point we go to the right
until we meet the inclined line 25, and follow this line to
its intersection A with the vertical line through 0. From
this point of intersection, go horizontally to the point of

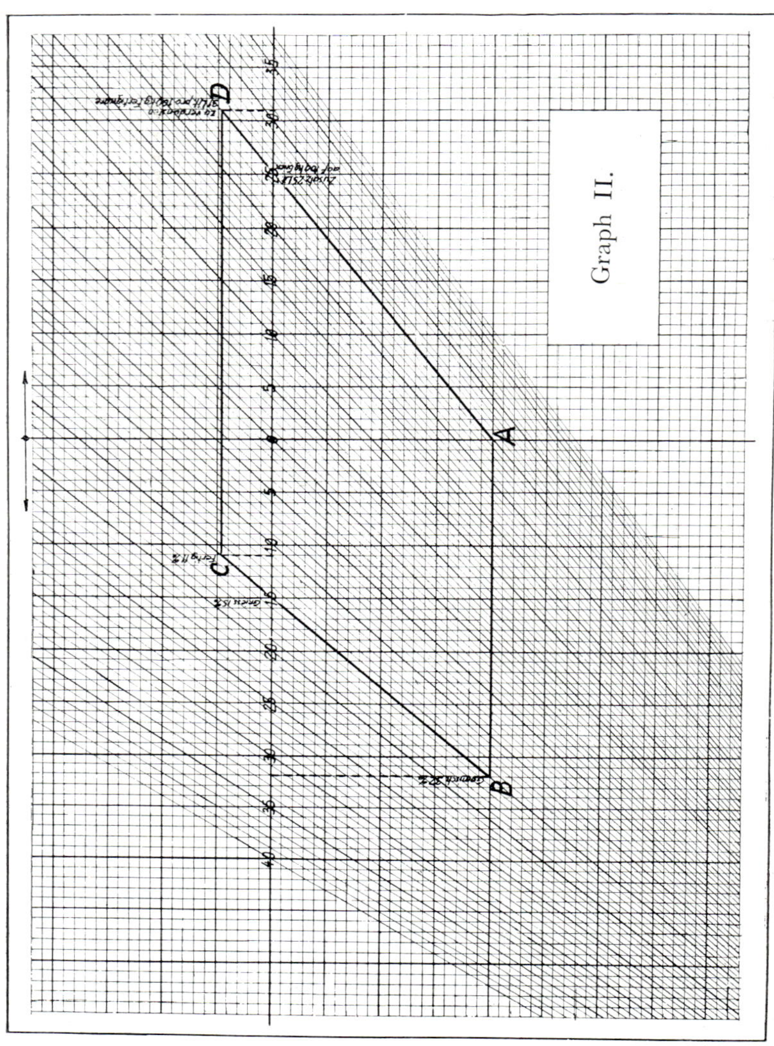

Graph II.

intersection B with the inclined line going through 15 on the left of o. From this last point B, go vertically to read the moisture content of the mixture, i.e. 32 per cent.

The quantity of water which has to be removed from this mixture to reduce its moisture to 11 per cent is found as follows:

Take the vertical left of o going through 11, from this intersection C with the inclined line going through 15, go horizontally to the intersection D with the inclined line going through 25. From intersection D go vertically to the intersection with the horizontal through o and read 31 kg., this representing the water that must be evaporated to bring the mixture at 32 per cent down to 11 per cent.

N

INDEX